Topic 1

Water and carbon cycles

Water and carbon cycles as natural systems

A system is a type of geographical model that removes incidental detail to highlight fundamental relationships. Systems are widely used in physical geography.

A system is an assemblage of interrelated parts that work together by way of some driving process. It consists of a series of stores or components that have flows or connections between them. There are three types of property: **elements** (the things that make up the system), **attributes** (the characteristics of the elements), and **relationships** (how the elements work together).

A system has a structure that lies within a boundary and functions by having inputs and outputs of material (energy and/or matter) that is processed within the components, causing it to change in some way.

The two main types of system used in physical geography are the closed system and the open system.

Closed systems

These have transfers of energy both into and beyond the system boundary but there is no transfer of matter.

1 On separate paper draw a labelled sketch of an example of a closed system in physical geography. (AO1, AO3) 4 marks

Open systems

These are where matter *and* energy can be transferred from the system across the boundary into the surrounding environment. Most ecosystems, for example, are open systems (see Figure 1.1).

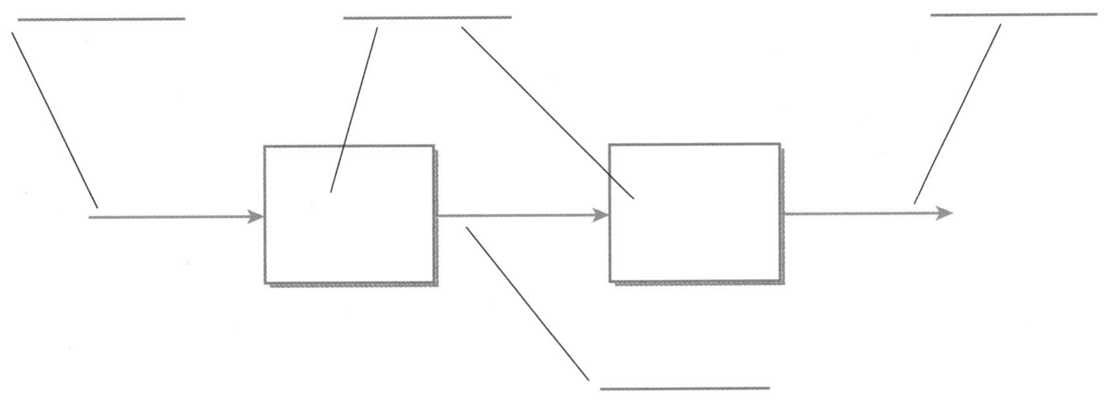

Figure 1.1 An open system

2 Complete Figure 1.1, using the following labels: (AO1) 3 marks

Component/Store | Output | Input | Flow

3 Suggest an example of an open system in physical geography. (AO1) 1 mark

....

When there is a balance between the inputs and outputs then the system is said to be in a state of **dynamic equilibrium**. If one of the elements of the system changes, e.g. one of the inputs increases without any corresponding change in the outputs, then the stores change and the equilibrium is upset. This is called **feedback**. There are two types of feedback: positive and negative.

Positive feedback occurs when the effects of an action are amplified or multiplied by subsequent 'knock-on' or secondary effects.

Negative feedback occurs when the effects of an action are nullified or dampened by subsequent 'knock-on' effects.

4 **Starting with the box labelled 'Global temperature rise', annotate Figure 1.2 with the following labels:**

- **Carbon dioxide back into the atmosphere**
- **Warms the oceans**
- **More carbon dioxide in the atmosphere**
- **More carbon dioxide to act as a greenhouse gas**
- **Warm water less able to dissolve gas**
- **Increased oceanic temperatures**
- **Dissolved carbon dioxide released by warmer oceans**

Give the figure a title.
(AO1, AO2, AO3) 8 marks

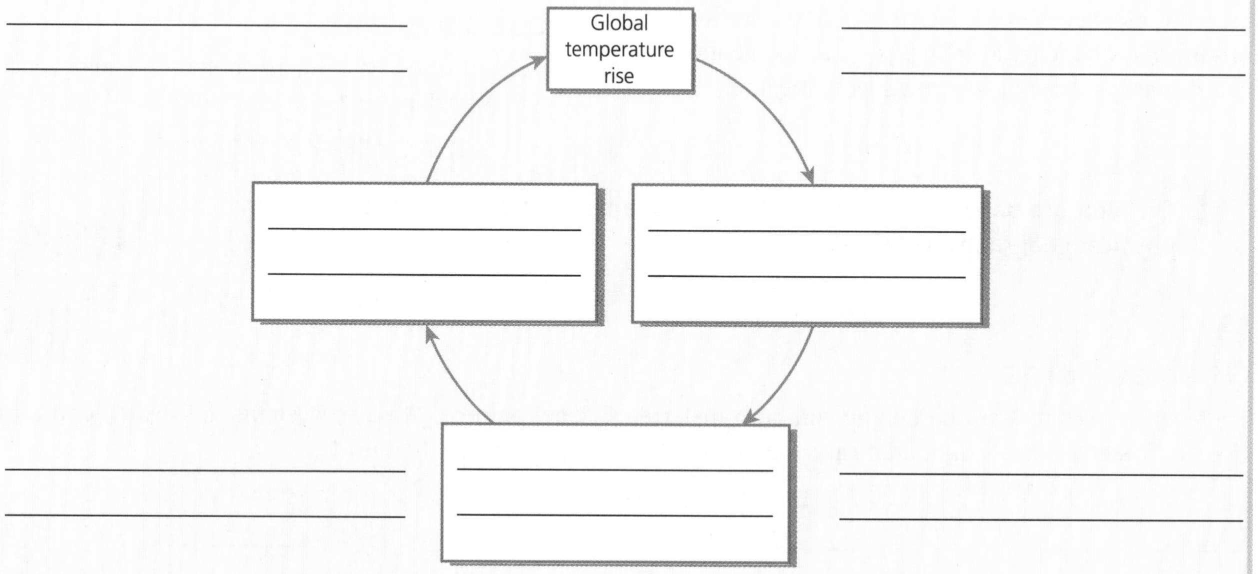

Global temperature rise

Figure 1.2 Example of positive feedback in a system

5 **Complete the following paragraph by filling in the gaps from the list below. (AO1, AO2, AO3)** 6 marks

Negative feedback

Following a rise in the ...., global carbon dioxide levels ....

This leads to a global temperature increase which, in turn, results in ....,

meaning that there is an increase in the .... This has a

.... and reduces ....

take-up of carbon dioxide | increase | dampening effect
use of fossil fuels | increased plant growth | global temperatures

The water cycle

Global stores of water

Water exists on Earth in three forms: liquid water (freshwater and salt water), solid ice (frozen ocean, ice sheets, ice caps, glaciers and permafrost) and gaseous water vapour. The amounts are summarised in Table 1.1.

Table 1.1

All water	
Location	**%**
Oceanic salt water	97
Fresh water	3

Fresh water	
Location	**%**
Crysospheric water	79
Ground water	20
Easily accessible surface water	1

Easily accessible surface water	
Location	**%**
Lakes	52
Soil	38
Atmosphere	8
Biomass	1
Rivers	1

6 Using the data from Table 1.1, describe the distribution of the Earth's water. (AO3) 4 marks

Movement of water between stores

A drainage basin (or catchment area) is the area that supplies a river with its water. This includes water found below the water table as well as soil water and any surface flow. A useful way of looking at drainage basins is to consider them as cascading systems. These are a series of open systems that link together so that the output of one is the input of the next. Like all systems they have inputs, outputs, stores and transfers.

7 Figure 1.3 (on page 6) shows how water moves about a small drainage basin and the nearby ocean. Using Table 1.2, complete Figure 1.3. (AO1, AO3) 18 marks

Table 1.2

Inputs	Stores	Transfers	Outputs
Precipitation on land	Lakes and surface water	Overland flow	Evaporation and transpiration from vegetation
Precipitation onto the sea	River channel	Channel flow	Evaporation from water surfaces
	Interception by plants	Infiltration	Runoff from the river
	Soil water	Percolation	Evaporation from the sea
	Groundwater	Throughflow	
		Groundwater flow	
		Throughfall/Stemflow	

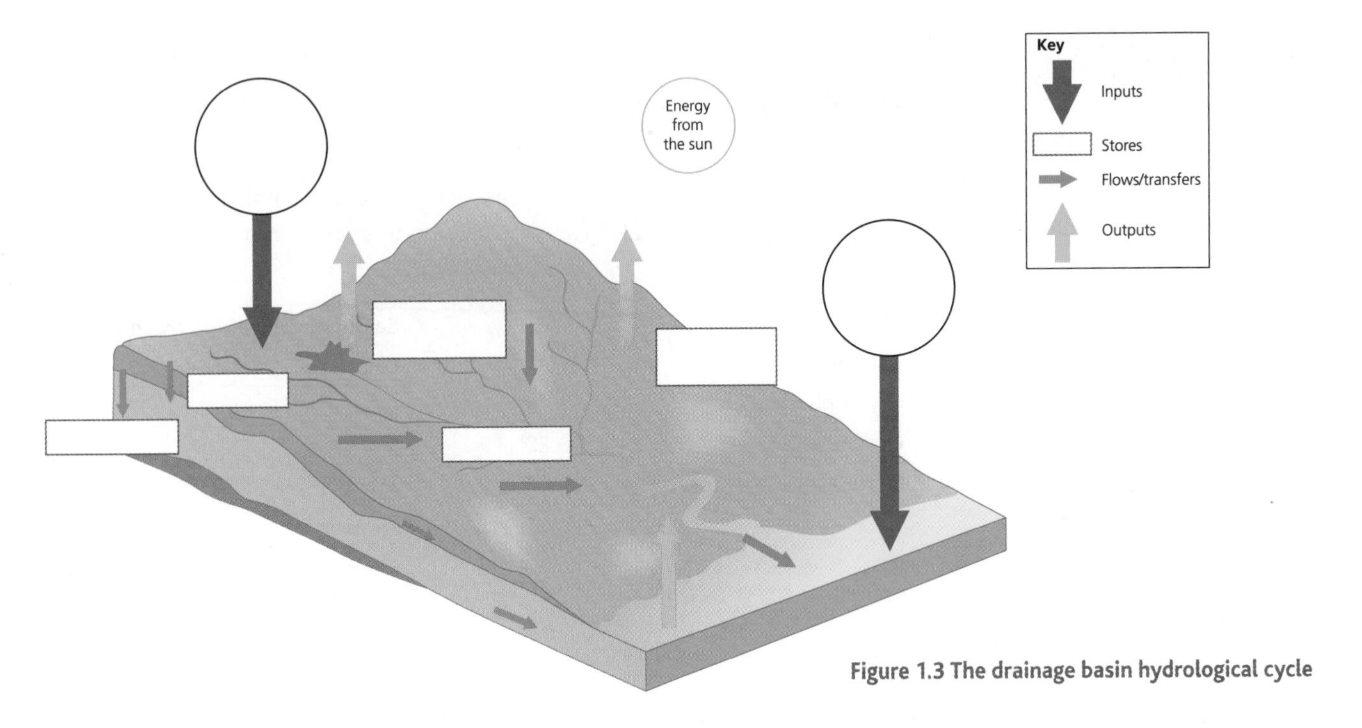

Figure 1.3 The drainage basin hydrological cycle

The water balance

Within a drainage basin, the balance between inputs (precipitation) and outputs (runoff, evapotranspiration, soil and groundwater storage) is known as the water balance or budget.

precipitation (P) = discharge (Q) + evapotranspiration (E) ± changes in storage (S)

A river is a natural stream of water flowing in a channel to the sea, a lake or another river. Rivers obtain water when:

- precipitation falls directly into the channel
- other water stores release it to travel by a variety of means to the channel

8 Describe the different ways that water can enter a river channel. (AO1 AO2) 5 marks

....

....

....

....

....

....

....

....

The flood hydrograph

River levels rise and fall, often showing an annual pattern (called the river's **regime**). They also vary in the short term following heavy rainfall. These short-term changes in river discharge can be displayed using a flood (or storm) hydrograph.

Although all storm hydrographs have the same common elements, they are not all the same shape. Hydrographs that have a short lag time, high peak discharge, and steep rising and falling limbs are described as being **'flashy'**. Others are a lot more **subdued** with gentle rising and falling limbs, long lag times and low peak discharge. This shape is determined by both physical and human factors.

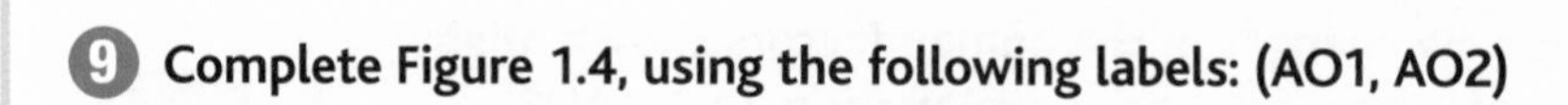

9 Complete Figure 1.4, using the following labels: (AO1, AO2)

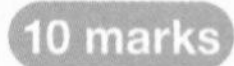

10 marks

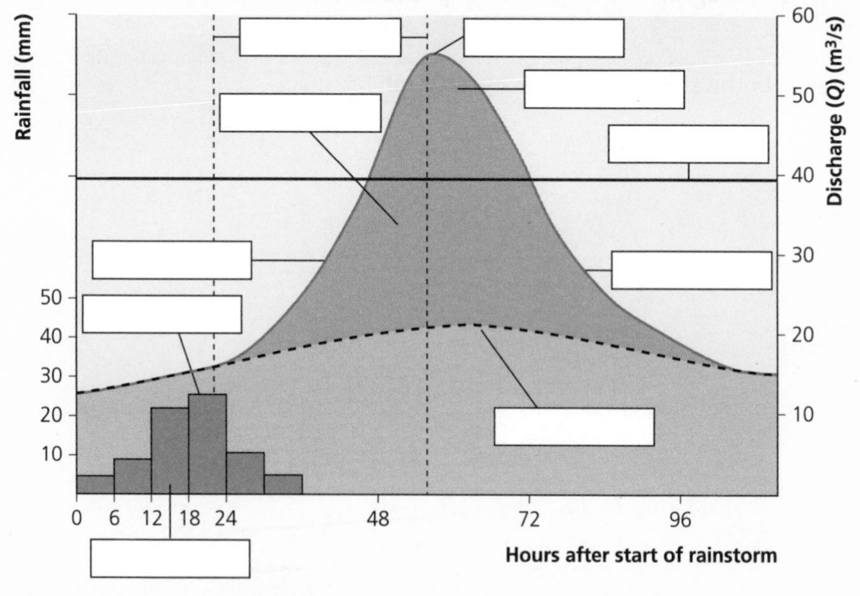

Figure 1.4 A storm hydrograph

Base flow | Recession limb | Peak rainfall | Rising limb | Peak discharge
Storm flow | Lag time | Flood water | Rainfall event | Bankfull discharge

10 Complete Table 1.3 by describing how changes in the named physical factors might change the shape of a storm hydrograph. Give a brief explanation. (AO1, AO2)

10 marks

Table 1.3

Physical factor	How it affects the shape of a storm hydrograph
Impermeable underlying rock	
Steep sides to the drainage basin	
A period of wet weather followed by intense rainfall	
A densely forested drainage basin	
The shape of a drainage basin	

11 **Complete Table 1.4 by describing how changes in the human factors shown might change the shape of a storm hydrograph. Give a brief explanation. (AO1, AO2)** 8 marks

Table 1.4

Human factor	How it affects the shape of a storm hydrograph
Deforestation	
Growth of urban areas	
Dam construction in the upper drainage basin	
Ploughing up of grassland	

The carbon cycle

Carbon forms more compounds than any other element and scientists predict that there are more than 10 million different carbon compounds in existence today on Earth. It is found in all life forms in addition to sedimentary rocks, diamonds, graphite, coal and petroleum (oil and natural gas).

12 **Describe the chemical make-up, occurrence and importance to the carbon cycle of: (AO1)** 9 marks

a **carbon dioxide (CO_2)**

....

....

....

b **calcium carbonate ($CaCO_3$)**

....

....

....

c **liquid petroleum**

....

....

....

The global carbon cycle is the pathway by which carbon moves through the Earth system, including the land, oceans, atmosphere and biosphere. Some components of the Earth system, such as the oceans and land, at times act as stores of carbon by storing it for long periods, and at other times act as carbon sources by releasing it back into the atmosphere.

Of growing importance in the global carbon cycle are the emissions from burning hydrocarbons. These are shown in Table 1.5.

Table 1.5 Global carbon emissions from fossil fuels, 1900–2010

Year	Global carbon emissions in millions of metric tonnes of carbon
1900	600
1910	850
1920	1,000
1930	1,100
1940	1,300
1950	1,600
1960	2,600
1970	4,050
1980	5,300
1990	6,100
2000	6,850
2010	9,200

13 **Complete the graph in Figure 1.5 from the data in Table 1.5. You must label the axes and plot the data. (AO3)** 6 marks

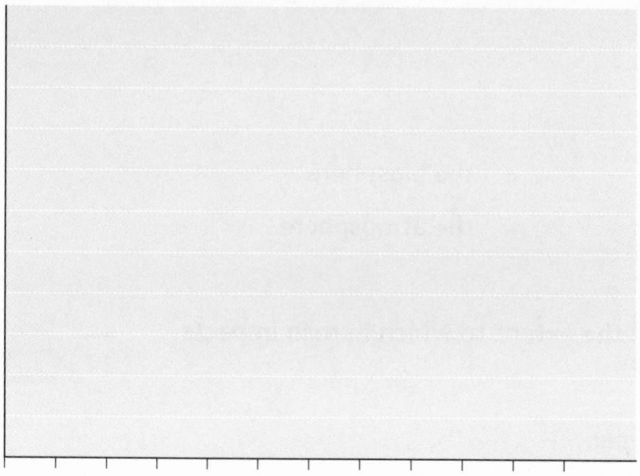

Figure 1.5

14 **Describe the changes in the amount of global carbon emissions as shown in Figure 1.5. What effect could this have on the Earth's climate? (AO2, AO3)** 6 marks

Exam-style questions (AS)

1 **Outline the potential impacts of human interventions in the carbon cycle. (AO1, AO2)** 4 3 marks

....

....

....

....

2 **Study a completed version of Figure 1.3. With the aid of Figure 1.3, describe the drainage basin hydrological cycle and the processes that operate in it. (AO1, AO3)** 7 6 marks

....

....

....

....

....

....

....

3 **The major global stores of carbon are:**

- **the lithosphere**
- **the hydrosphere**
- **the cryosphere**
- **the biosphere**
- **the atmosphere**

Take any TWO of these stores and assess the extent to which human impacts have changed them over time. (AO1, AO2) 10 9 marks

Write your answer on a separate sheet of paper.

4 **As part of your course you have studied a drainage basin at a local level. Describe the impact of precipitation upon the water stores and transfers in that drainage basin and explain the implications for either a sustainable water supply and/or flooding. (AO1, AO2)** 22 20 marks

Write your answer on a separate sheet of paper.

Exam-style questions (A-level)

5 **Explain the concept of negative feedback in relation to the carbon cycle. (AO1, AO2)** 5 4 marks

....

....

....

....

Write your answers to questions 6–8 on a separate sheet of paper.

6 Study Figure 1.6. Analyse the varying potential for global carbon sequestration from different types of forestry management, 1995–2050. (AO2, AO3)

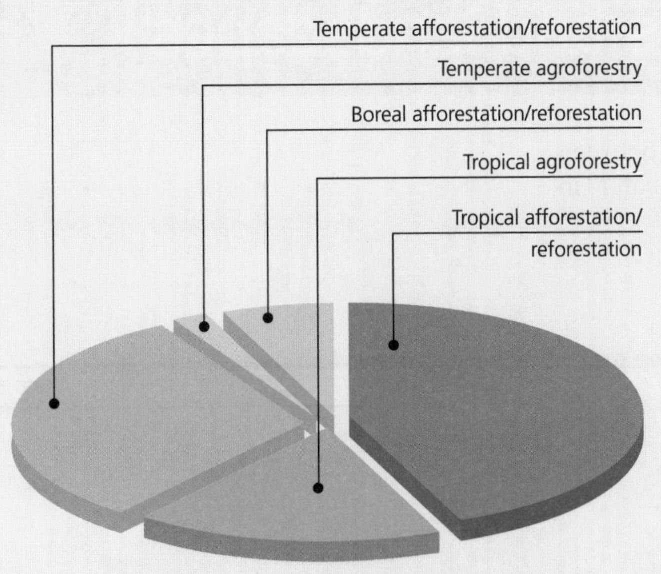

Total carbon sequestration potential 38 Gt

Figure 1.6 Potential contribution of afforestation/reforestation and agroforestry activities to global carbon sequestration, 1995–2050

7 Figure 1.7 shows the predicted change in global rainfall intensity by the end of the twenty-first century. Using Figure 1.7, analyse this predicted change. (AO2, AO3)

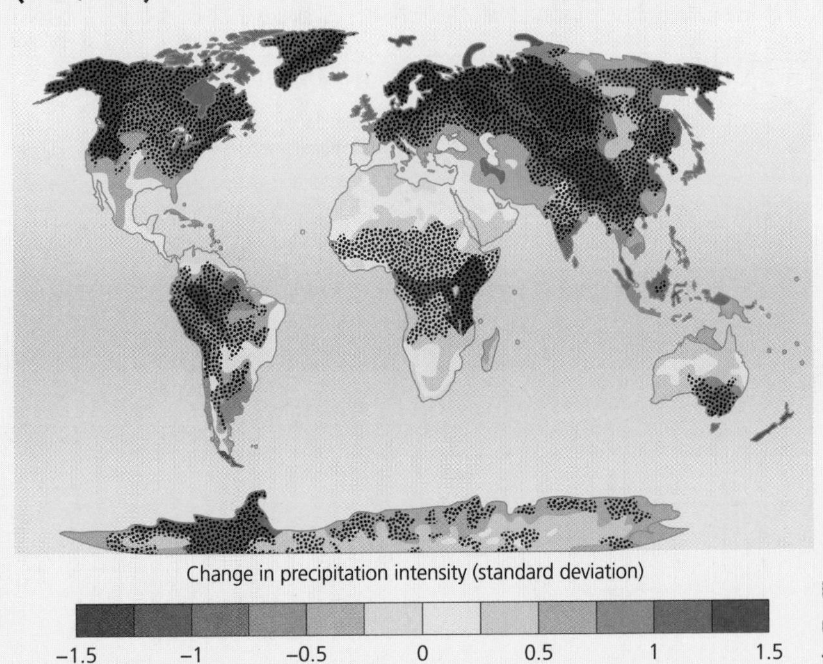

Figure 1.7 The predicted change in rainfall intensity by the end of the twenty-first century

8 With reference to a river catchment you have studied, assess the extent to which runoff depends on natural variation in the water cycle rather than human activity. (AO1, AO2)

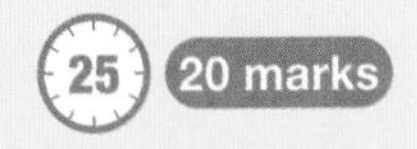

Topic 2

Hot desert systems and landscapes

The majority of hot desert areas lie between 15° and 30° north and south of the equator in the centre or on the west coasts of continents.

1 Describe the global distribution of the main areas of hot desert shown in Figure 2.1. (AO1, AO3) 6 marks

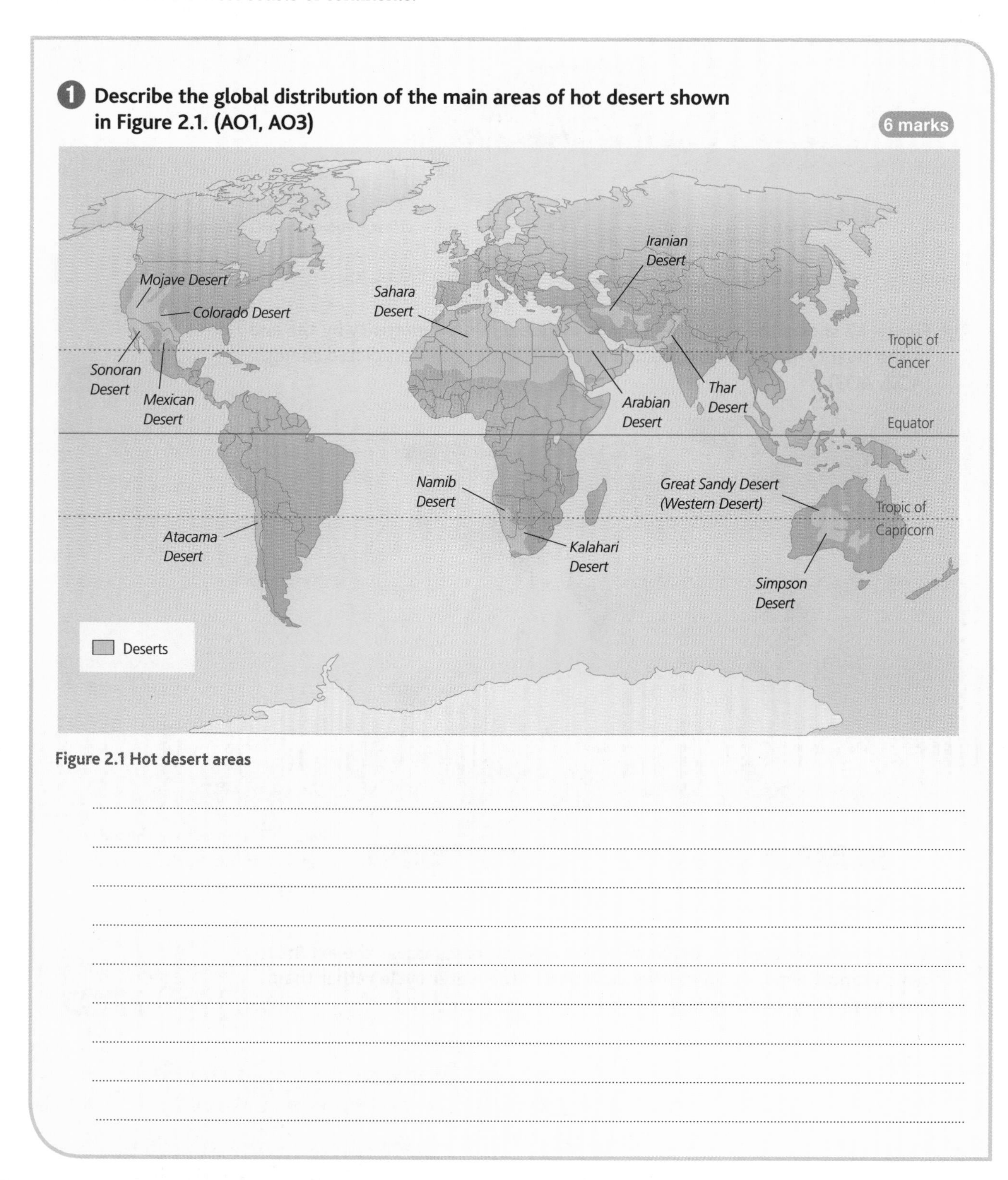

Figure 2.1 Hot desert areas

Deserts as natural systems

Like all systems in physical geography, desert systems have inputs, processes, flows and outputs. These act together to form a rich variety of landscapes ranging from bare rocky plains to extensive sand seas, and from complex badlands topography to deep canyons. The climate of hot deserts is one of the major inputs into the system.

2 Table 2.1 gives details about the climate of Sabha.

Table 2.1 The climate of Sabha

Month	Jan	Feb	Mar	Apr	May	June	July	Aug	Sep	Oct	Nov	Dec
Average maximum temperature (°C)	19	21	26	32	36	39	39	39	38	33	26	20
Average minimum temperature (°C)	6	8	12	17	22	25	25	25	24	19	12	7
Average precipitation (mm)	7	0.5	9	7	1	0.5	0.5	0	0	0	2	1

a Complete the climate graph for Sabha (Figure 2.2). (AO3) 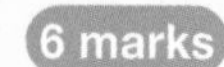

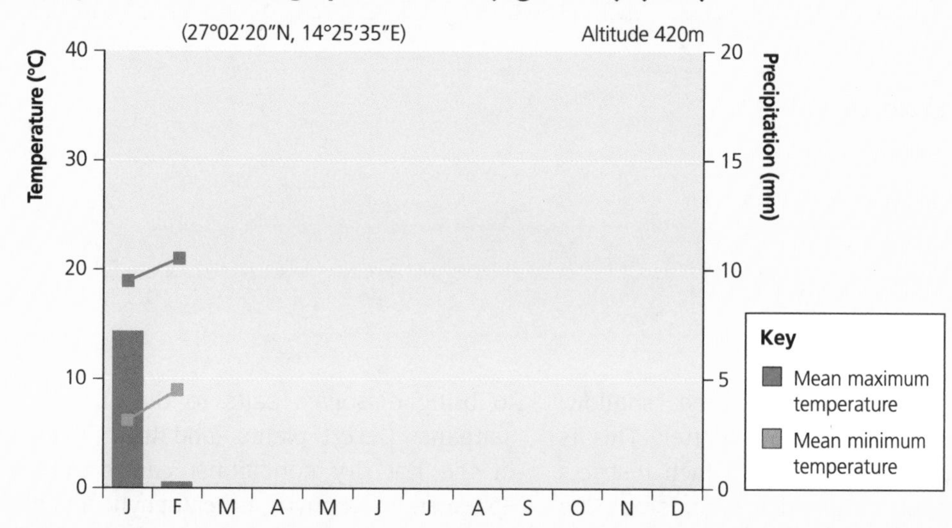

Figure 2.2 Climate graph for Sabha

b In which country and in which desert is Sabha located? (AO3) 1 mark

....

c Describe the main features of the climate of Sabha. (AO1, AO2, AO3) 4 marks

....

....

....

....

....

....

....

There are four main causes of aridity in hot deserts. These act alone or combine together.

3 For each of the following, explain how it contributes to aridity in hot desert areas. For each cause, name a desert affected by it. (AO1, AO2) 12 marks

a **Subsiding air and associated high atmospheric pressure linked to the descending limbs of the Hadley cell**

....

....

....

b **The rainshadow effect**

....

....

....

c **Continentality**

....

....

....

d **Cold ocean currents**

....

....

....

Soils in hot deserts are coarse-textured, shallow, rocky or gravely, with little organic matter. This is caused by the low plant productivity, which restricts the soil-building properties of microorganisms. The intense evaporation of water from desert soils tends to bring dissolved salts to the surface, leading to saltpans. Desert plants (and their ability to survive in the hot dry conditions) can be categorised as: ephemeral, xerophytic, phreatophytic and halophytic.

4 Using examples, describe the adaptations that the following types of plants have made in order to survive in hot deserts. (AO1, AO2) 12 marks

a **Ephemerals**

....

....

....

b **Xerophytes**

....

....

....

c **Phreatophytes**

....

....

....

d **Halophytes**

....

....

....

The water balance compares the mean annual precipitation (P) received with the mean annual potential evapotranspiration (PET). PET is the amount of water that could be lost from the soil by plant transpiration and direct evaporation from the ground. Deserts can be classified based on this balance using an aridity index (AI). The United Nations has defined the aridity index as:

$$AI = \frac{P}{PET}$$

Hot deserts and their margins are considered to be areas described as hyper-arid to arid, as defined in Table 2.2

Table 2.2

Classification	AI	Global land area
Hyper-arid	AI < 0.05	7.5%
Arid	0.05< AI <0.20	12.1%

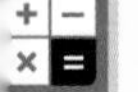

5 a **Complete Table 2.3 by stating whether the area can be defined as hyper-arid (HA), arid (A) or not arid at all (N). (AO3)**

Table 2.3

Precipitation (mm) (P)	Potential evapotranspiration (PET)	Aridity index	HA/A/N?
200	5,000		
150	2,500		
250	1,050		
250	2,500		

b **What conclusions can be drawn from the completed Table 2.3? (AO2)** 2 marks

....

....

Systems and processes

There are three main sources of energy that drive the desert system: insolation, wind and water movement (runoff). **Insolation** is intense in the subtropical desert areas. Its impact is reinforced because the air is dry and there is sparse vegetation cover. Many weathering processes that occur in hot deserts result from changes or differences in temperature. Days tend to be very hot but the nights are much cooler.

6 **Explain why daytime temperatures in hot deserts are so high. (AO1, AO2)** 3 marks

....

....

....

....

7 **Explain why the temperatures become much lower at night-time. (AO1, AO2)** 3 marks

....

....

....

....

Weathering, the physical disintegration and chemical decomposition of rocks *in situ* at or near the Earth's surface, occurs in hot deserts. Chemical weathering is limited by the small amounts of water available in hot deserts but mechanical weathering in the form of exfoliation, thermal fracture, block and granular disintegration occurs more often.

8 **Outline how each of the weathering processes named below operates. (AO1, AO2)** 9 marks

a **Exfoliation**

....

....

....

....

....

b **Thermal fracture**

....

....

....

....

....

c **Block and granular disintegration**

....

....

....

....

....

Wind is almost always present in deserts. The location of deserts means that they are either the source of winds as air falls on the descending limb of the Hadley cell and blows out from the desert *or* they are blown over by the trade winds. Winds play a role in desert landscape formation by being able to pick up (erode) and transport material (which can then itself be a tool in erosion). When their speed falls they deposit any load they are carrying.

9 **In hot deserts winds erode by deflation and abrasion (sand-blasting). Explain how those processes contribute to the shaping of desert landscapes and name one landform shaped predominantly by each process. (AO1, AO2)** 8 marks

a Deflation

....

....

....

....

b Abrasion

....

....

....

....

10 **Attrition occurs when individual particles hit against each other or a solid surface. How does this affect the sediment? (AO1, AO2)** 3 marks

....

....

....

Winds are able to transport desert material. The method of transport and the distance the particles are carried depends on the strength of the wind and the diameter of the particles. Fine clay and silt particles are lifted high in the air and carried in **suspension**. Sand and coarse silt is carried by the process of **saltation** at a height of usually no more than 2 m. Coarser material is rolled along the surface by **traction**.

11 **Explain the process of saltation. (AO1)** 3 marks

....

....

....

Water plays (or has played) a major role in shaping desert landscapes. Present-day water comes from:

- localised and rare, but heavy, rainstorms
- exogenous rivers that flow straight through the desert (e.g. the Colorado River)
- endoreic rivers that may start either outside or within the desert but which flow into an internal drainage basin

In wetter periods of the past, water played a major role in shaping the landscape. This original surface has then been altered by the more recent wind, flood water and weathering to create what we see today.

Arid landscape development in contrasting settings

Although all the above processes are active for at least some of the time, there are landscapes where one set of processes dominates the others.

Landscapes and landforms shaped predominantly by wind erosion

These include deflation hollows, desert pavements, yardangs, zeugen and ventifacts.

Landscapes and landforms shaped predominantly by deposition

There are many types of dune found in deserts, including barchan dunes and seif dunes.

12 **Yardangs and zeugen depend on the geological structure of rocky desert areas. Describe the differences between the two landforms and show how these differences are related to the geology. (AO1, AO2)** 6 marks

....

....

....

....

....

....

13 **Annotate Figure 2.3 with the following labels: (AO1, AO3)** 3 marks

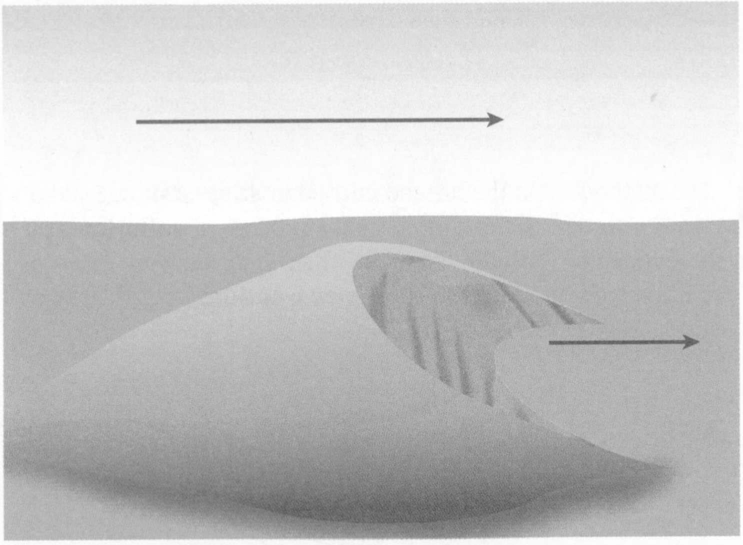

Direction of dune migration

Maximum height 30 m

Concave slip slope

Windward slope

Wind direction

Horn

Figure 2.3 A sketch of a barchan dune

14 **Explain how barchan dunes can change into seif dunes. (AO1, AO2)** 4 marks

....

....

....

....

Landscapes and landforms shaped predominantly by water

These include wadis, bajadas, pediments, playas and inselbergs.

A wadi is a dry valley that has been formed by an ephemeral stream.

15 **Outline the main features of wadis and explain the role of water in their formation. (AO1, AO3)** 5 marks

....

....

....

....

....

....

16 **Study Figure 2.4. Using the diagram, explain how bajadas are formed. (AO1, AO3)** 4 marks

Figure 2.4 The formation of a bahada

....

....

....

....

....

17 **Assess the extent to which water plays a role in the formation of mesas, buttes and inselbergs. (AO1, AO2)** 6 marks

....

....

....

....

....

....

Desertification

The United Nations Convention to Combat Desertification defines the term desertification as '**land degradation** in **arid**, **semi-arid** and dry **sub-humid** areas resulting from various factors including climatic variations and human activities'. It affects terrestrial areas (topsoil, earth, **groundwater reserves**, surface runoff), animal and plant populations, as well as human settlements and their amenities (for instance, terraces and dams).

18 Describe the global pattern of those areas at risk of desertification shown in Figure 2.5. (AO1, AO3) 6 marks

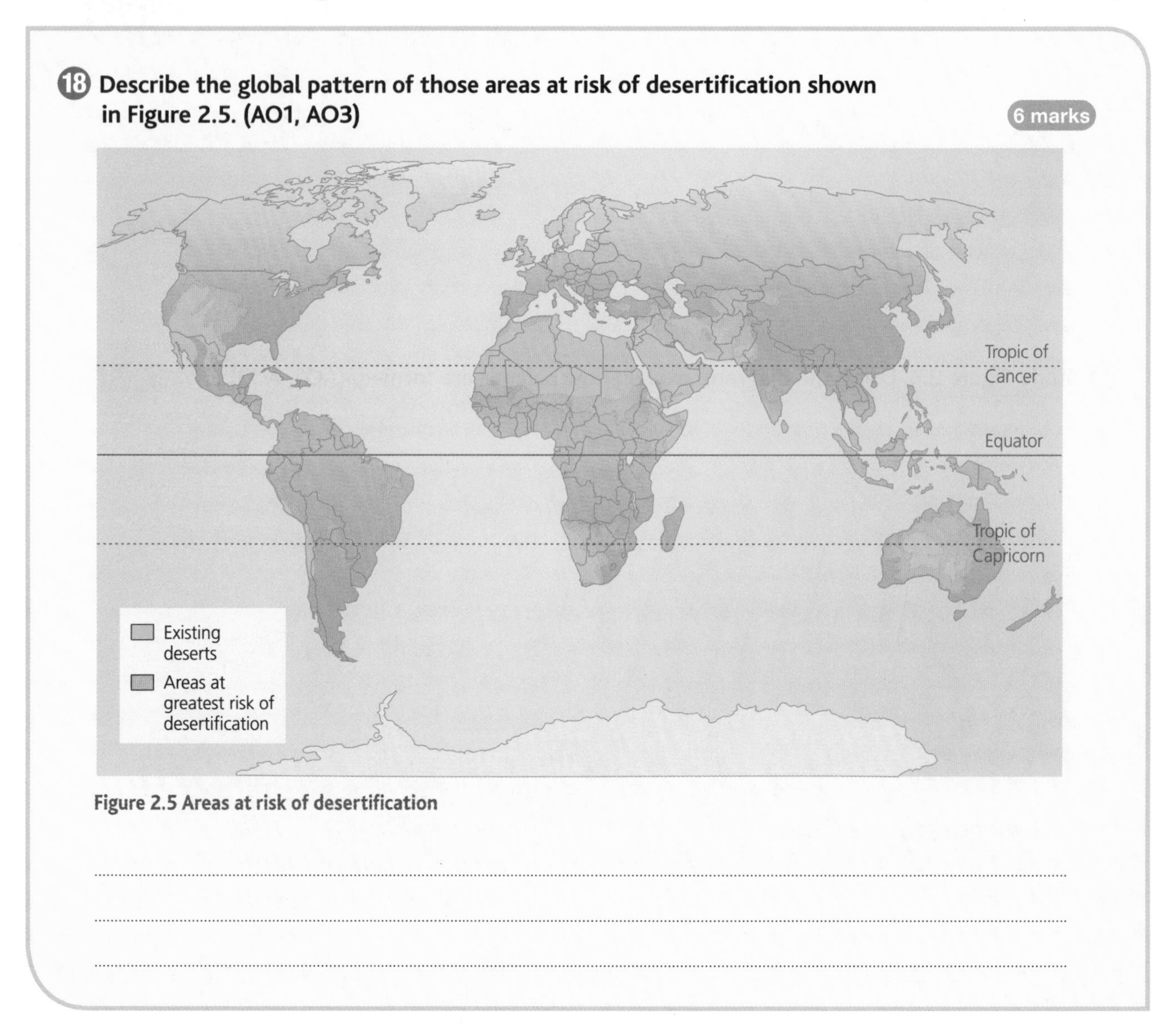

Figure 2.5 Areas at risk of desertification

....

....

....

A recent study of how climate change affects arid regions concluded that:

- deserts are more likely to have increased rainfall
- higher temperatures will also increase evaporation and cause more catastrophic weather events
- weather extremes such as wildfires, cold snaps, heatwaves and storms would intensify

19 How might climate change affect the rate and extent of desertification of those areas at risk? (AO1, AO2) 6 marks

....

....

....

....

Table 2.4 Estimates of land area subject to desertification belonging to vulnerability classes and corresponding number of impacted population

Vulnerability class	Area subject to desertification		Population affected	
	Area (million km²)	Percent (global land area)	Number (millions)	Percent (global population)
Low	14.60	11.2	1,085	18.9
Moderate	13.61	10.5	915	15.9
High	7.12	5.5	393	6.8
Very high	7.91	6.1	255	4.4
TOTAL	44.24	34.0	2,648	44.0

20 Study Table 2.4. What conclusions can be drawn from these data? (AO2, AO3) 6 marks

Exam-style questions (A-level)

1 Outline ONE cause of aridity in hot desert areas. (AO1) 5 4 marks

2 Study Figure 2.6. Outline the impacts of water on the development of the landscape shown. (AO1, AO2, AO3) 7 6 marks

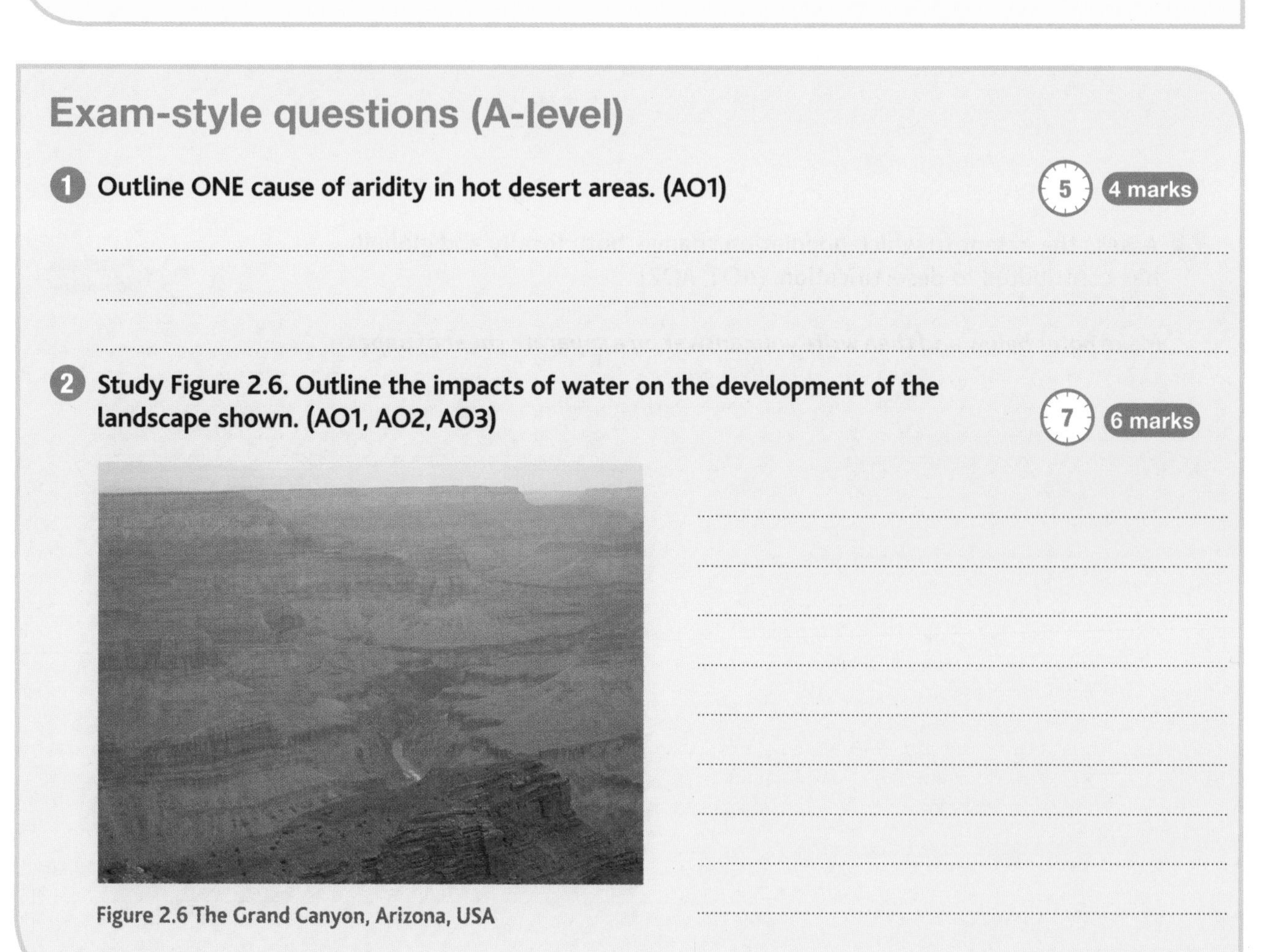

Figure 2.6 The Grand Canyon, Arizona, USA

3 **Using only information from the text below, analyse the various adaptations made by desert plants in order to survive the harsh conditions. (AO1, AO2, AO3)** 7 **6 marks**

Plants in hot deserts are mainly low woody shrubs and trees. Leaves are 'replete' (fully supported with nutrients) and water-conserving. They tend to be small, thick and covered with a thick cuticle (outer layer). In cacti, the leaves are reduced to spines and photosynthesis is restricted to the stems. Cacti also depend on chlorophyll in the outer tissue of their skin and stems to conduct photosynthesis for the manufacture of food. Spines protect the plant from animals, shade it from the sun and also collect moisture. Extensive shallow root systems are usually radial and because they store water in the core of both stems and roots they survive long periods of drought.

Some plants open their stomata only at night. These plants include: yuccas, ocotillo and prickly pears.

The large numbers of spines on plants in desert areas shade the plant's surface. The same is true of the hairs on the woolly desert plants and many plants have silvery or glossy leaves.

Phreatophytes, like the mesquite tree, have adapted to desert conditions by developing extremely long root systems. The mesquite's roots are considered the longest of any desert plant and have been recorded as long as 20 metres.

Other plants survive by becoming dormant during dry periods, then springing to life when water becomes available. After rain falls, the ocotillo, for example, quickly grows a new suit of leaves, flowers bloom within a few weeks, and when seeds become ripe and fall, the ocotillo loses its leaves again and re-enters dormancy. This process may occur as often as five times a year.

....

....

....

....

....

....

....

....

4 **Assess the extent to which population change, both locally and globally, has contributed to desertification. (AO1, AO2)** 7 **20 marks**

Make notes below and then write your answer on a separate sheet of paper.

....

....

....

....

....

....

....

....

....

....

....

Topic 3

Coastal systems and landscapes

Coasts as natural systems

Like all systems in physical geography, coastal systems have inputs, processes, flows and outputs. These act together to form a rich variety of component landforms and landscapes.

1 Complete the following paragraph by filling in the gaps from the list below. (AO1, AO3) 20 marks

Inputs into a coastal system include:

- **energy from ...., ..., ... and ....**
- **sediment either eroded from the local coastal rocks or transported from either .... or along the ....**
- **the .... and .... of the local geology**
- **sea level change**

Erosional processes such as .... and .... result in erosional coastlines and landscapes as well as eroded material. .... alters the eroded material by making it .... and less ....

Sediment is transported by either .... or .... until it reaches a low .... environment where it is ....

The outputs from the system are in the form of:

- **................ .... dissipated by breaking along the shoreline**
- **sediment accumulation above ....**
- **sediment moved on to other ....**

finer	energy	waves	wind
hydraulic action	wave energy	offshore	structure
ocean currents	deposited	high tide level	angular
abrasion	wind	coast	tides
water	sediment cells	rock type	attrition

Systems and processes

Sources of energy

Wind is a primary source of energy. Energy transferred from wind to water not only creates waves but also drives the vast oceanic circulation systems called gyres. It also provides the energy to transport fine material along terrestrial surfaces such as beaches and sand dunes. Swell waves are the result of winds generating waves far out to sea. They tend to travel in the direction of the winds that originally formed them.

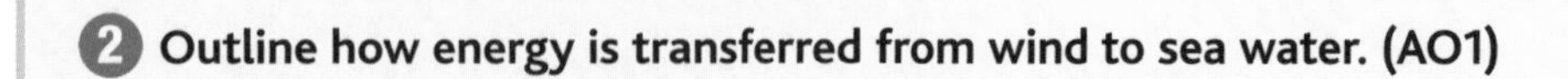

2 **Outline how energy is transferred from wind to sea water. (AO1)** 

2 marks

....

....

....

3 **Table 3.1 gives the percentage wind direction for Newquay, Cornwall.**

Table 3.1

Direction	Percentage
N	6.2
NNE	3.7
NE	2.9
ENE	2.4
E	3.9
ESE	5.2
SE	5.2
SSE	6.3

Direction	Percentage
S	6.7
SSW	7
SW	6.8
WSW	10.5
W	9.6
WNW	8.1
NW	8.7
NNW	6.6

Complete Figure 3.1 by constructing a wind rose diagram for Newquay. (AO3) 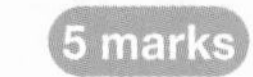

5 marks

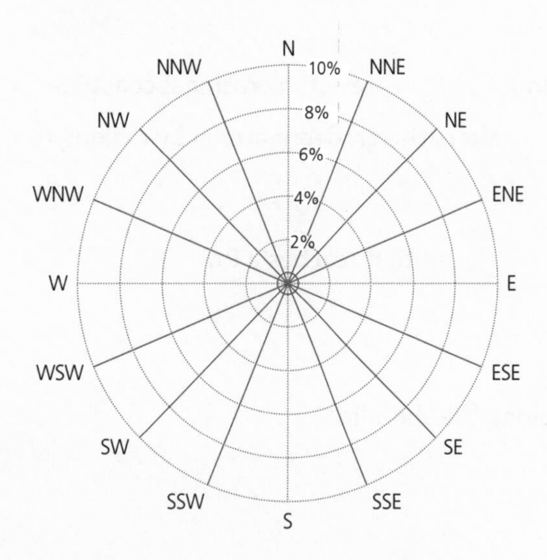

Figure 3.1 A wind rose diagram showing the mean annual percentage of wind direction for Newquay, Cornwall

Waves are expressions in the sea's surface that indicate that energy is being transferred from one place to another. They have little impact on landscapes until they come into contact with land. As the sea shallows, the frictional drag at the base of the wave causes it to shorten, steepen and eventually break. These breaking waves are divided into two broad types, constructive (spilling) waves and destructive (plunging waves).

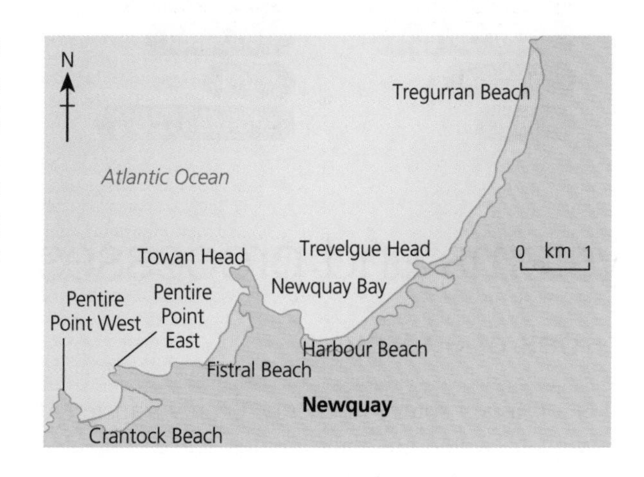

Figure 3.2 A sketch map of the beaches around Newquay, Cornwall

4. **Use labelled diagrams to show the difference between a constructive wave and a destructive wave. (AO1, AO2, AO3)** 6 marks

5. **Describe and explain the different impacts that constructive waves and destructive waves have on a beach. (AO1, AO2)** 6 marks

6. **Using Figures 3.1 and 3.2, state which of the named beaches around Newquay is likely to be the best for surfing. Give reasons for your choice. (AO1, AO2, AO3)** 6 marks

In the sea, a current is the permanent or seasonal movement of water. Ocean currents rarely have any effect on coastal landscapes. Rip currents are strong localised currents that carry water away from the shore. They have a role in the creation of beach cusps.

The main current to affect coastlines is the longshore current. This can give rise to the transport process of longshore drift.

Tides are a periodic rise and fall in the depth of the sea. The amount of rise and fall varies throughout a lunar month depending on the relative positions of the sun and the moon to the Earth.

Similar to all budgets, a coastal sediment budget is the balance between what sediment goes into a stretch of coastline and what sediment comes out.

7 Use labelled diagram(s) to explain the causes of high and low tides, and spring and neap tides. (AO1, AO3) 4 marks

Sediment sources

8 Define the term sediment cell. (AO1) 2 marks

....

....

....

9 Describe a sediment cell that you have studied. (AO1) 3 marks

....

....

....

10 What are the main sources of sediment along a coastline? (AO1) 2 marks

....

....

....

Geomorphological processes

Weathering, the physical disintegration and chemical decomposition of rocks in situ at or near the Earth's surface, occurs on coastlines. There are three types of weathering: mechanical/physical, biological and chemical.

Sea water is slightly alkaline and so is not usually able to react with carbonate rocks, though carbonation does occur to coastal limestones.

11 The main form of mechanical weathering is freeze–thaw action. What causes freeze–thaw action along coastlines and why is it quite rare on British coastlines, especially along the south coast of England? (AO1, AO2) 4 marks

....

....

....

....

12 Apart from freeze–thaw action, name one other type of mechanical weathering process that occurs specifically on coastlines. Describe the process and explain how it affects the coastal landscape. (AO1, AO2) 4 marks

....

....

....

....

13 Under what circumstances does carbonation occur on coastlines? (AO1) 2 marks

....

....

Mass movement, the movement of rocks under the influence of gravity, occurs on coastlines.

One of the most common is rotational slumping.

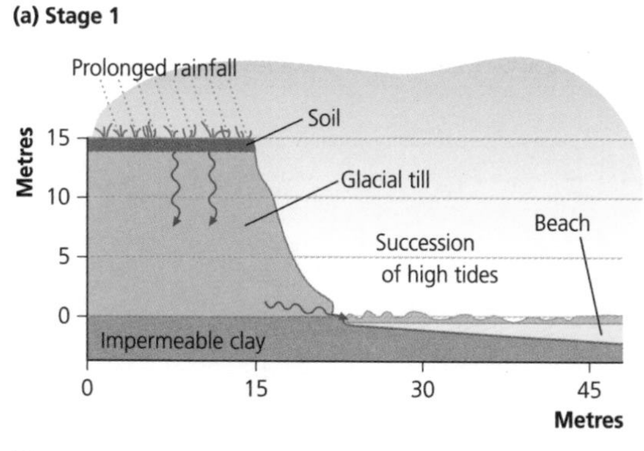

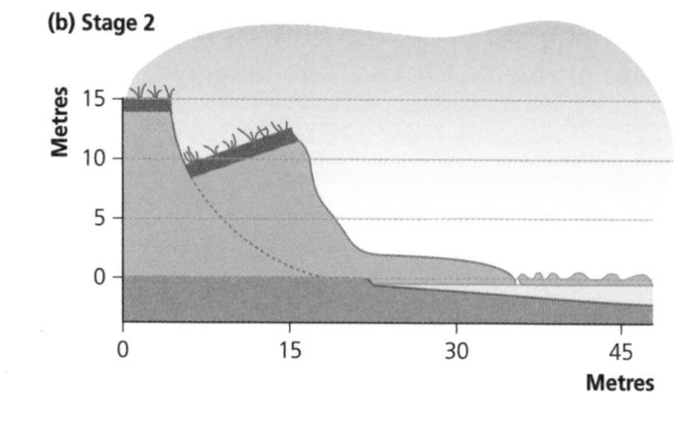

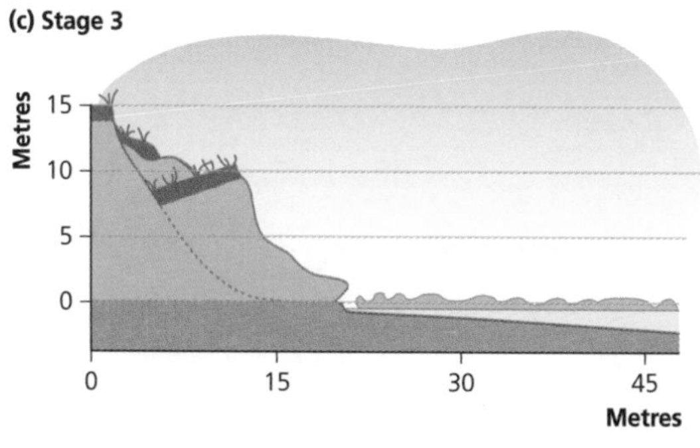

Figure 3.3 Rotational slumping

14 **Using Figure 3.3 and an example you have studied, explain the process of rotational slumping for that location. (AO1, AO2, AO3)** 6 marks

....

....

....

....

....

....

....

....

....

15 **The most common form of marine sediment transport is longshore drift. Draw an annotated diagram to explain the process of longshore drift. (AO1, AO3)** 4 marks

16 **Wind moves lighter material on a beach by the processes of saltation and traction. Describe these processes and explain why onshore winds causing this movement may create problems for coastal managers. (AO1, AO2)** 5 marks

....

....

....

....

....

....

....

....

Deposition of coastal material occurs when the medium carrying that sediment (water or air) either loses energy or becomes less turbulent.

Coastal landscape development

Landforms and landscapes of coastal erosion

Figure 3.4 Selwick's Bay, Flamborough Head, Yorkshire

17 **Figure 3.4 shows caves, arches and a wave-cut platform on the Yorkshire coast.**

a **Outline the sequence of events in the evolution of this coastline. (AO1, AO2, AO3)** 4 marks

....

....

....

....

....

....

b **Although stacks are not present in the photograph, explain how stacks could be formed at Flamborough Head. (AO1, AO2)** 4 marks

....

....

....

....

....

....

Landforms and landscapes of coastal deposition

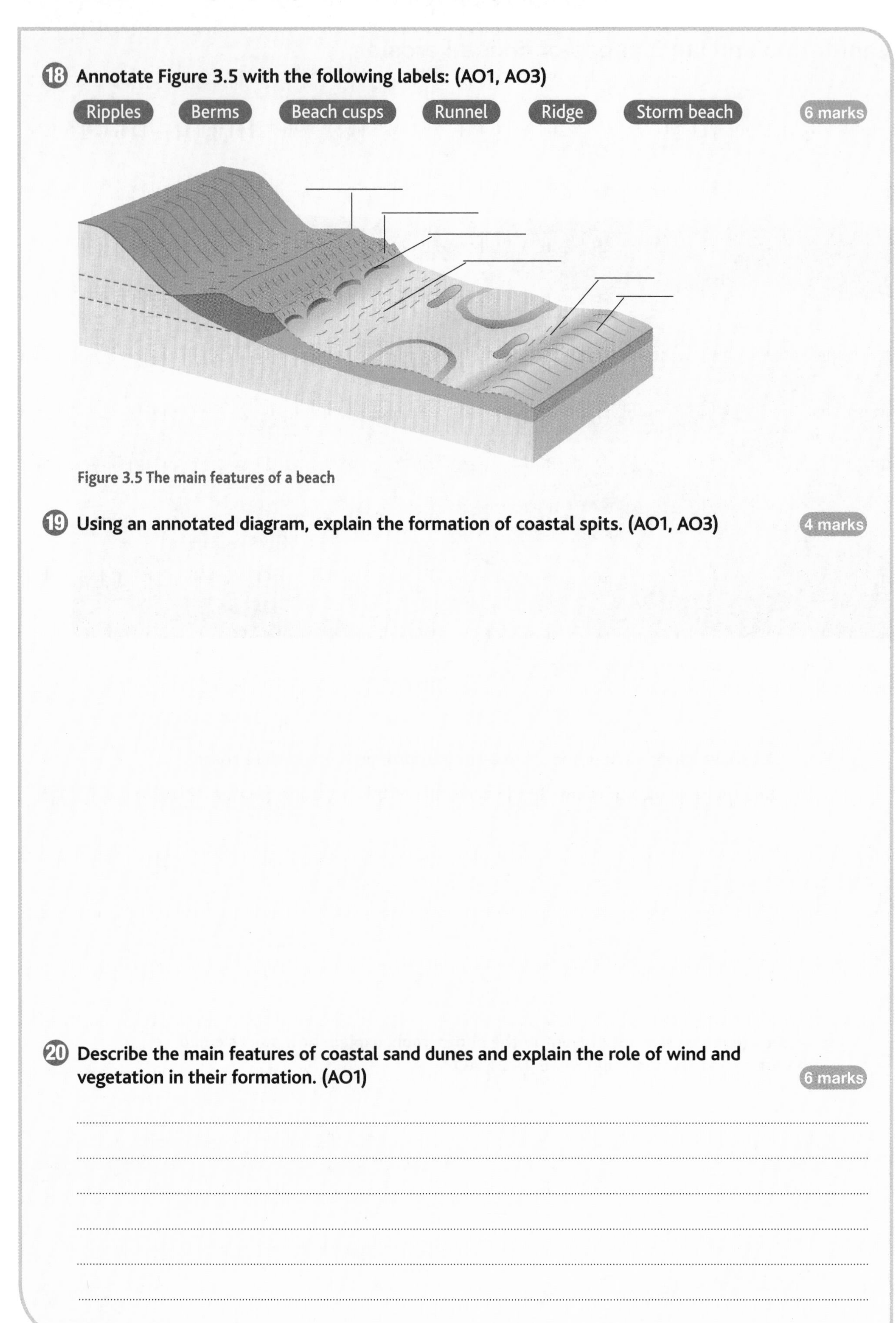

18 **Annotate Figure 3.5 with the following labels: (AO1, AO3)**

Ripples Berms Beach cusps Runnel Ridge Storm beach

6 marks

Figure 3.5 The main features of a beach

19 **Using an annotated diagram, explain the formation of coastal spits. (AO1, AO3)**

4 marks

20 **Describe the main features of coastal sand dunes and explain the role of wind and vegetation in their formation. (AO1)**

6 marks

Estuarine landscapes

21 **Describe and explain the formation of a saltmarsh and tidal (mud) flats. (AO1, AO3)** 5 marks

....

....

....

....

....

Sea-level change

Raised beaches and marine platforms have been caused by falling sea levels whereas rias, fjords and Dalmatian coastlines are formed by rising sea levels.

22 **Draw an annotated sketch of either a ria or a fjord or a Dalmatian coastline describing the main features and explaining the role of changing sea level. (AO1, AO3)** 5 marks

Coastal management

Securing the sustainable use of the coastal zone provides particular challenges. There are often complex issues related to whose responsibility it is to manage the coastline. An estimated 60% of the world's human population live on or close to the coast and the pressures on coastal environments for economic development are particularly high.

Hard engineering

Hard engineering could be defined as controlled disruption of natural processes by using human-made structures. These structures include: sea walls, groynes, breakwaters.

Soft engineering

Soft engineering uses natural systems for coastal defence such as beaches and dunes which can absorb and adjust to wave and tide energy. It involves manipulating and maintaining these systems, without changing their fundamental structures.

23 Describe the hard coastal defences along a stretch of coastline. Analyse the extent to which the defences have achieved the goals set by coastal managers. (AO1) **8 marks**

....

....

....

....

....

....

....

....

24 Using an example of a scheme of soft engineering you have studied, assess the sustainability of the scheme. (AO1) **8 marks**

....

....

....

....

....

....

....

....

Exam-style questions (AS)

1 Outline the role of weathering in the development of some coastlines. (AO1) 4 **3 marks**

....

....

....

2 Study Figure 3.6. Describe the coastline and assess the role played by sea-level change in the formation of this coastline. (AO2, AO3) 7 **6 marks**

Figure 3.6 A sketch of part of the coastline of the Isle of Arran

3 To what extent do major changes in sea level in the last 10,000 years contribute to the development of landforms such as raised beaches, marine platforms, rias, fjords and Dalmatian coasts? (AO1, AO2) 10 9 marks

Write your answer on a separate sheet of paper.

4 To what extent does climate change present risks and opportunities for human occupation in a named coastal landscape beyond the UK? (AO1, AO2) 22 20 marks

Write your answer on a separate sheet of paper.

Exam-style questions (A-level)

5 Explain the concept of eustatic sea-level change. (AO1) 5 4 marks

6 Some students carried out fieldwork on the shingle beach and ridge at Porlock in North Devon shown on the sketch map Figure 3.7. One of the characteristics that they measured was the roundness of the pebbles at the western end (Gore Point) and the eastern end (Hurlstone Point) of the beach. 7 6 marks

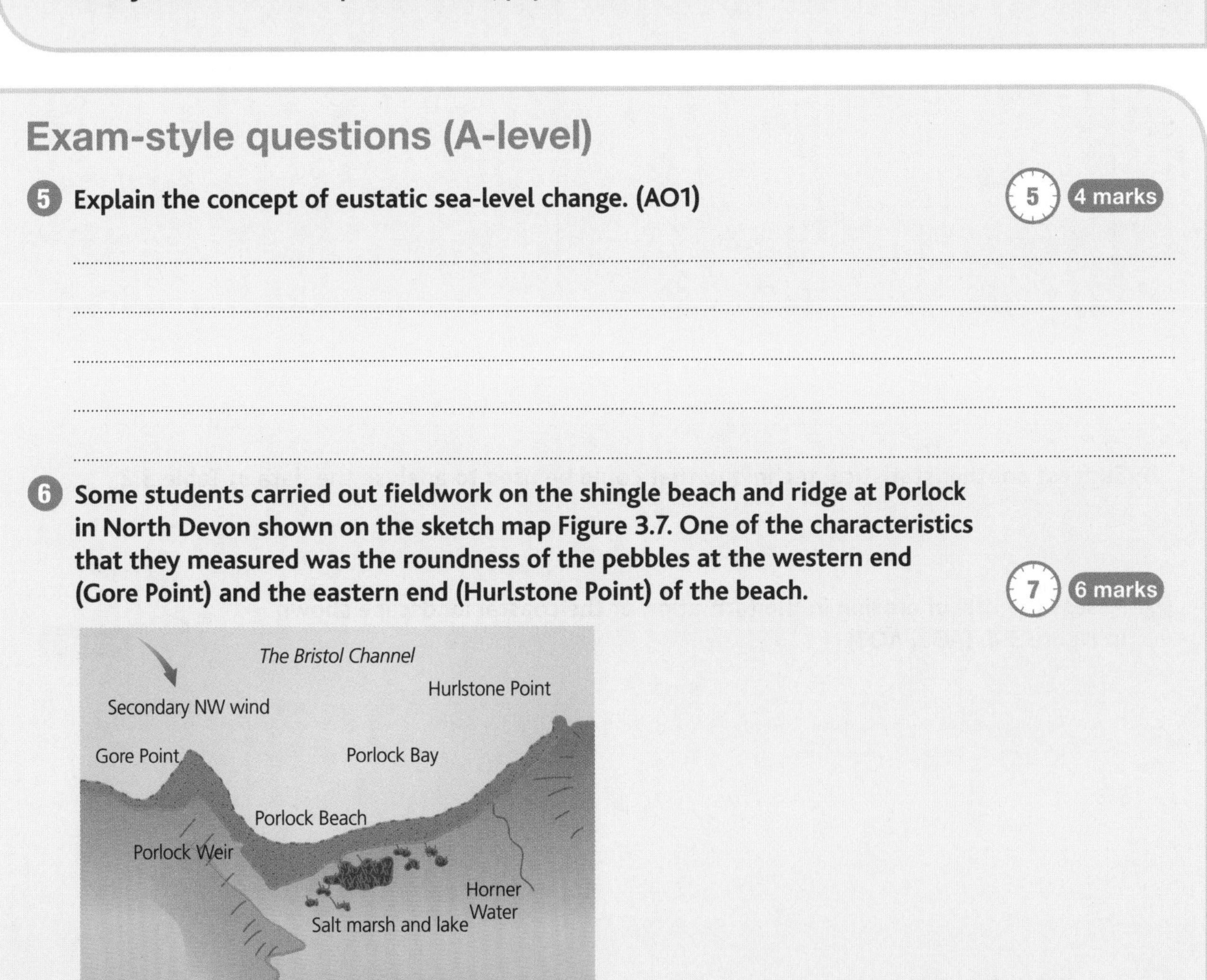

Figure 3.7 A sketch map of Porlock Bay and Beach

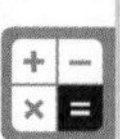

A sample of 150 pebbles was collected at each point and the Cailleux roundness index was measured, where 0 is completely angular and 1,000 is a perfect sphere. The results are shown in Table 3.2.

a Draw two histograms, one for Gore Point and one for Hurlstone Point to show the frequency of different pebble roundness at each end of Porlock Beach. What conclusions can be drawn from your histograms? (AO2, AO3)

Table 3.2

Shape	Gore Point	Rank	Hurlstone Point
0–100	2	10	1
101–200	14	5	2
201–300	28	2	8
301–400	36	1	25
401–500	25	3	23
501–600	19	4	16
601–700	9	6	26
701–800	4	9	27
801–900	8	7	15
901–1000	5	8	7

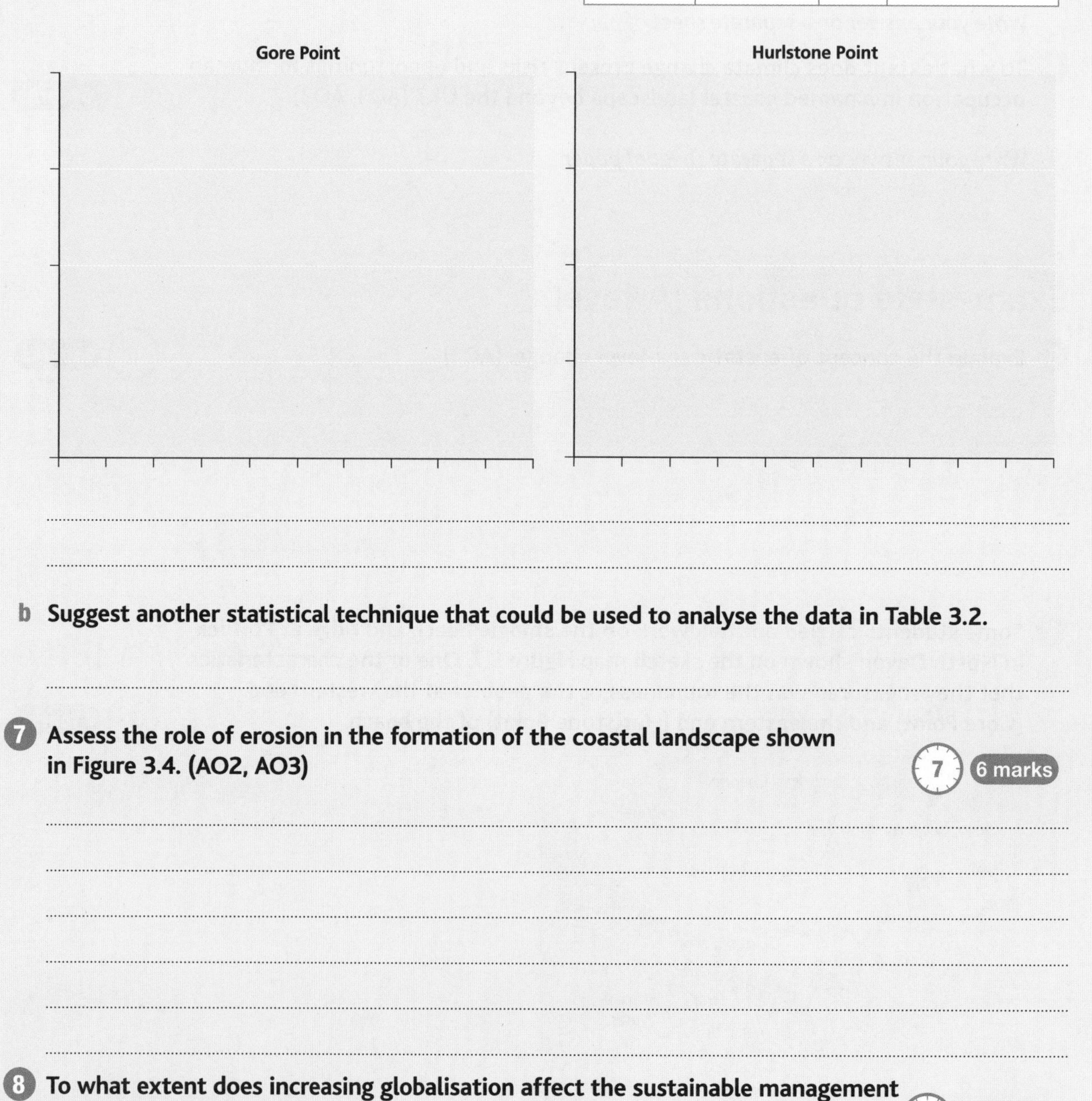

....

....

b Suggest another statistical technique that could be used to analyse the data in Table 3.2.

....

7 Assess the role of erosion in the formation of the coastal landscape shown in Figure 3.4. (AO2, AO3)

7 | 6 marks

....

....

....

....

....

....

8 To what extent does increasing globalisation affect the sustainable management of coastlines? (AO1, AO2)

25 | 20 marks

Write your answer on a separate sheet of paper.

Topic 4

Glacial systems and landscapes

Glaciers as natural systems

Like all systems in physical geography, glacial systems have inputs, processes, flows and outputs. These act together to form a rich variety of component landforms and landscapes.

One of the main inputs into the glacial system is the amount of insolation a location receives. Glacial processes include a variety of weathering and erosion processes.

1 How does aspect affect the amount of insolation received on mountain sides? In the northern hemisphere, which slopes receive the least insolation? (AO1) 3 marks

....

....

....

2 What are the differences between weathering and erosion? (AO1) 3 marks

....

....

....

3 What role do rock fragments play in glacial erosion processes? (AO1) 3 marks

....

....

....

The nature and distribution of cold environments

Both present and past cold environments may be described as polar, alpine, glacial and periglacial.

At the height of the last ice advance, glacial areas were much more extensive.

4 Describe the global distribution of: (AO1) 6 marks

a **glacial areas**

....

b **alpine areas**

....

c **tundra areas**

....

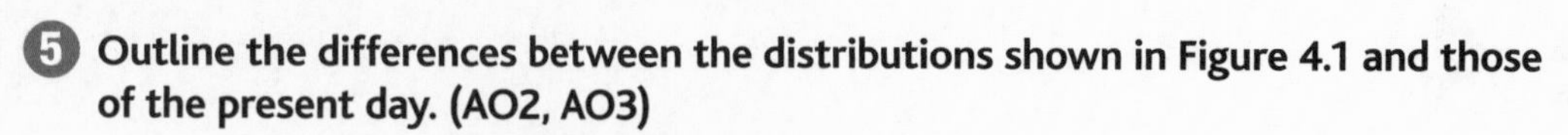

5 Outline the differences between the distributions shown in Figure 4.1 and those of the present day. (AO2, AO3)

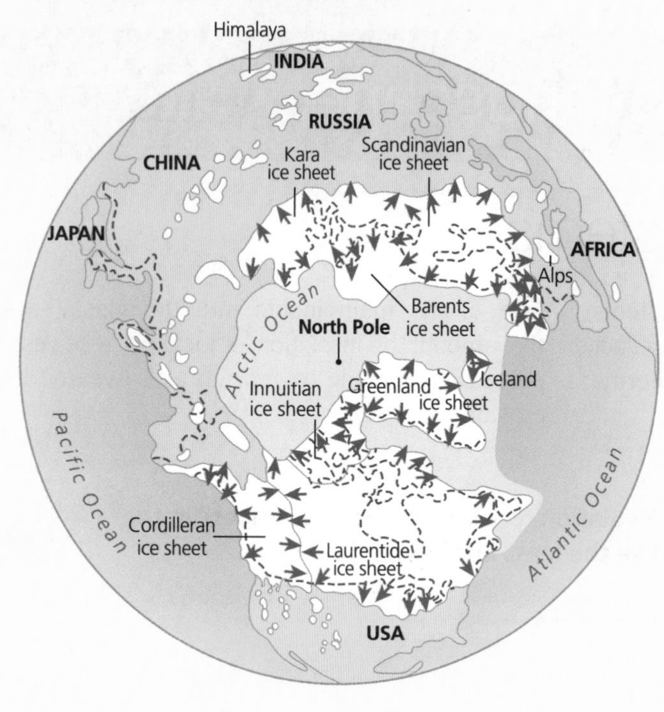

Figure 4.1 The distribution of continental ice sheets in the northern hemisphere at the height of the Pleistocene epoch

....

....

....

6 Describe the climates for Eismitte, Greenland (Figure 4.2a) and Barrow, Alaska, USA (Figure 4.2b). Outline the differences between them. (AO2, AO3)

5 marks

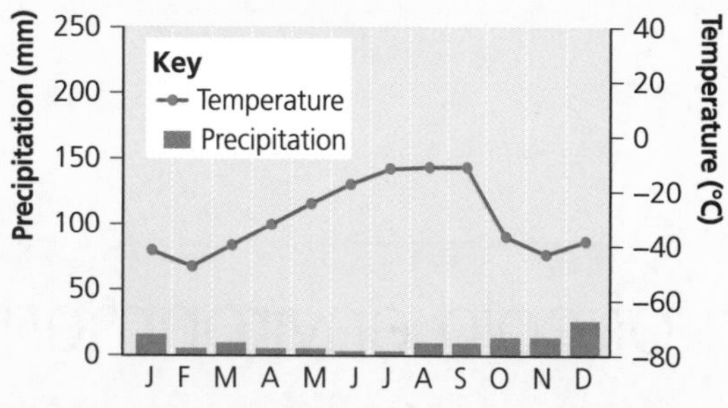

Figure 4.2a Climate graph for a tundra region: Eismitte, Greenland

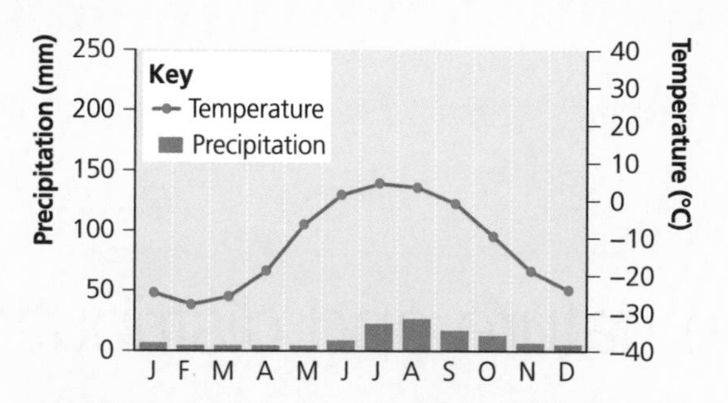

Figure 4.2b Climate graph for a polar region: Barrow, Alaska, USA

....

....

....

There are no soils in glacial environments: the ice scrapes any loose material away as it moves over the surface. Tundra environments have long winters and cool summers, allowing only limited vegetation growth. This, coupled with the high acidity and impermeability of the sub-surface permafrost, lead to a distinctive soil type. The tundra region is one of very low productivity because of the long cold winters and the frozen subsoil. Tundra vegetation is composed of dwarf shrubs, sedges and grasses, mosses and lichens. There are also some areas of scattered trees.

7 **Complete the soil profile of a tundra soil (Figure 4.3) using the following labels: (AO1, AO3)** **5 marks**

- **Lack of clearly differentiated soil horizons (layers), caused by lack of soil biota to mix layers**
- **A thin surface organic layer which is often very acidic**
- **Waterlogged in summer, as water unable to percolate into permafrost**
- **Gleyed (because of the waterlogging, iron compounds are reduced to their ferrous form, which is blue/grey)**
- **Impermeable frozen ground**

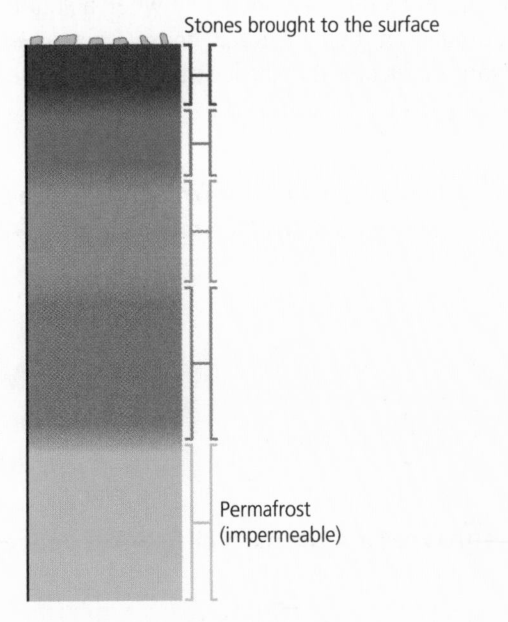

Figure 4.3 The profile for a tundra soil

Systems and processes

Geomorphological processes

A glacier can be viewed as a system with inputs, stores, transfers and outputs.

8 **Complete Figure 4.4, using the following labels: (AO1, AO3)** 

- **Area where inputs exceed outputs, leading to a net gain in mass**
- **The glacier itself, consisting of ice, water, air and rock debris**
- **Snow and ice from both precipitation and avalanche; rock debris from the valley side and floor**
- **Water vapour, calving, melting (to form meltwater streams) and rock debris**
- **The separation line between areas of net loss and net gain**
- **Area where outputs exceed inputs, leading to a net loss of mass**
- **Glacial movement**

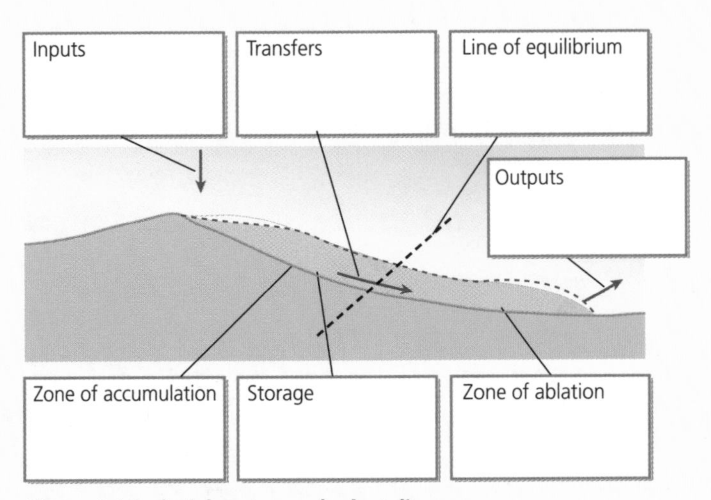

Figure 4.4 A glacial system or budget diagram

If accumulation exceeds ablation then the net mass of the glacier increases. Conversely, when ablation exceeds accumulation then the net mass decreases. Glacial advance indicates that the ice mass has extended further downhill and covers more area. Glacial retreat indicates that the mass of ice is reduced and the glacier's snout is found at a greater (colder) altitude.

9 Explain how long-term temperature changes have caused glacial advance and retreat throughout the Pleistocene epoch. (AO1, AO2) 6 marks

....

....

....

....

....

10 What are the main differences between warm- and cold-based glaciers? (AO1) 5 marks

....

....

....

....

....

Glacial landforms and landscapes are the result of a combination of weathering, ice movement, erosion, transport and deposition. The main weathering process that takes place is frost action.

Nivation is a periglacial process that operates under snow patches located where there are regular (seasonal) periods of melting. It is a combination of frost action and chemical weathering accompanied by meltwater 'flushing'.

11 Describe how frost action operates and how it influences the development of glacial landforms. (AO1, AO2) 7 marks

....

....

....

....

....

....

12 Describe how nivation operates and how it influences the development of corries. (AO1, AO2) 7 marks

....

....

....

....

....

....

Glacial movement

Ice moves downhill under the influence of gravity. This movement relies on two properties of ice. The first is that, under pressure, ice acts like a plastic and can bend. The second is that under pressure the melting temperature of ice is lowered, meaning that it can turn to liquid water at the bottom of a glacier simply because of the weight of the ice above. The overall pattern of movement within a glacier depends on the steepness of the slopes it flows down.

13 Explain how the following types of ice movement operate. (AO1) 9 marks

a Internal deformation

....

....

....

b Basal sliding and regelation flow

....

....

....

c Bed deformation

....

....

....

14 Using Figure 4.5, explain how extending and compressing flow are related to changes in valley gradient. (AO2) 5 marks

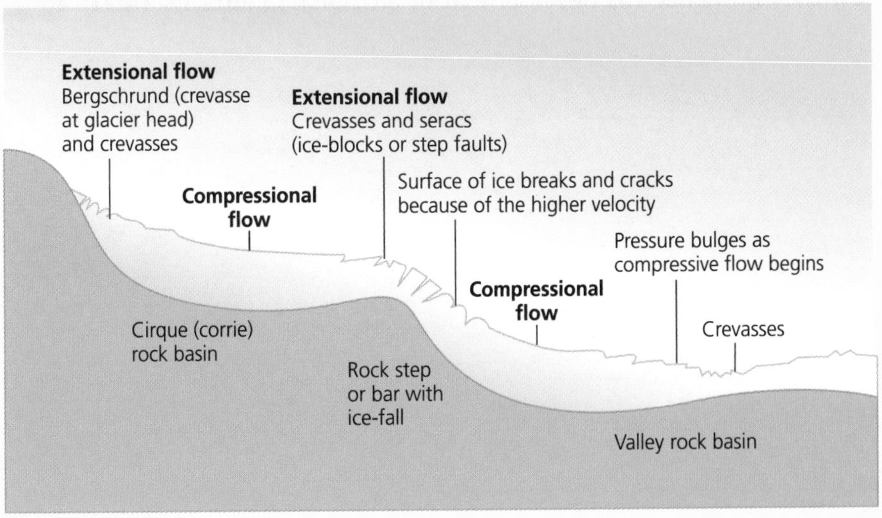

Figure 4.5 Extending and compressing flow

....

....

....

....

....

....

....

15 **Rotational flow occurs in corries. It is a combination of both extending and compressing flow. Draw a labelled diagram to show how ice moves in a corrie. (AO1, AO3)** 4 marks

Glacial erosion and deposition

Erosion processes play a major role in the way glaciers shape the land.

16 **The two main processes are plucking and abrasion. Explain how each of these processes work and how they influence the development of erosional landforms. (AO1)** 6 marks

....

....

....

....

....

....

....

....

Ice carries loose rock along with it when it moves. Unlike a river, the load it carries has a range of sizes. It is unsorted. The load can be carried on the surface of the ice or it can be washed into and incorporated by the body of the glacier. A large amount of load can be found at the base of the ice. This has either been washed or fallen down from the surface or it has originated as the product of plucking and abrasion.

Deposition of this material occurs when the ice melts. The resultant deposited rock is known as moraine or till.

Fluvioglacial processes

Warm-based glaciers are very wet places, particularly in summer at lower altitudes. Surface ice melts and the water finds its way through the ice to the base. Here it collects in subglacial streams and eventually emerges at the snout of the glacier. These streams are under great pressure and so have a lot of energy to transport and erode some of the glacier's rock load.

17 **Explain the circumstances under which a glacial meltwater stream might deposit its load. (AO1, AO2)** 6 marks

....

....

....

....

....

....

Periglaciation and permafrost

Regions close to glaciated areas are known as periglacial regions. These are dominated by very low temperatures for most of the year with a short, slightly warmer, summer. The ground below the top 0.5–3.0 metres is called permafrost because all the groundwater stored within it is permanently frozen. The surface layer, known as the active layer, melts seasonally, becoming waterlogged. This allows the soil/weathered material to be churned up by the variation in temperatures.

18 **Describe the variations in depth of the permafrost as shown in Figure 4.6. (AO1, AO3)** 3 marks

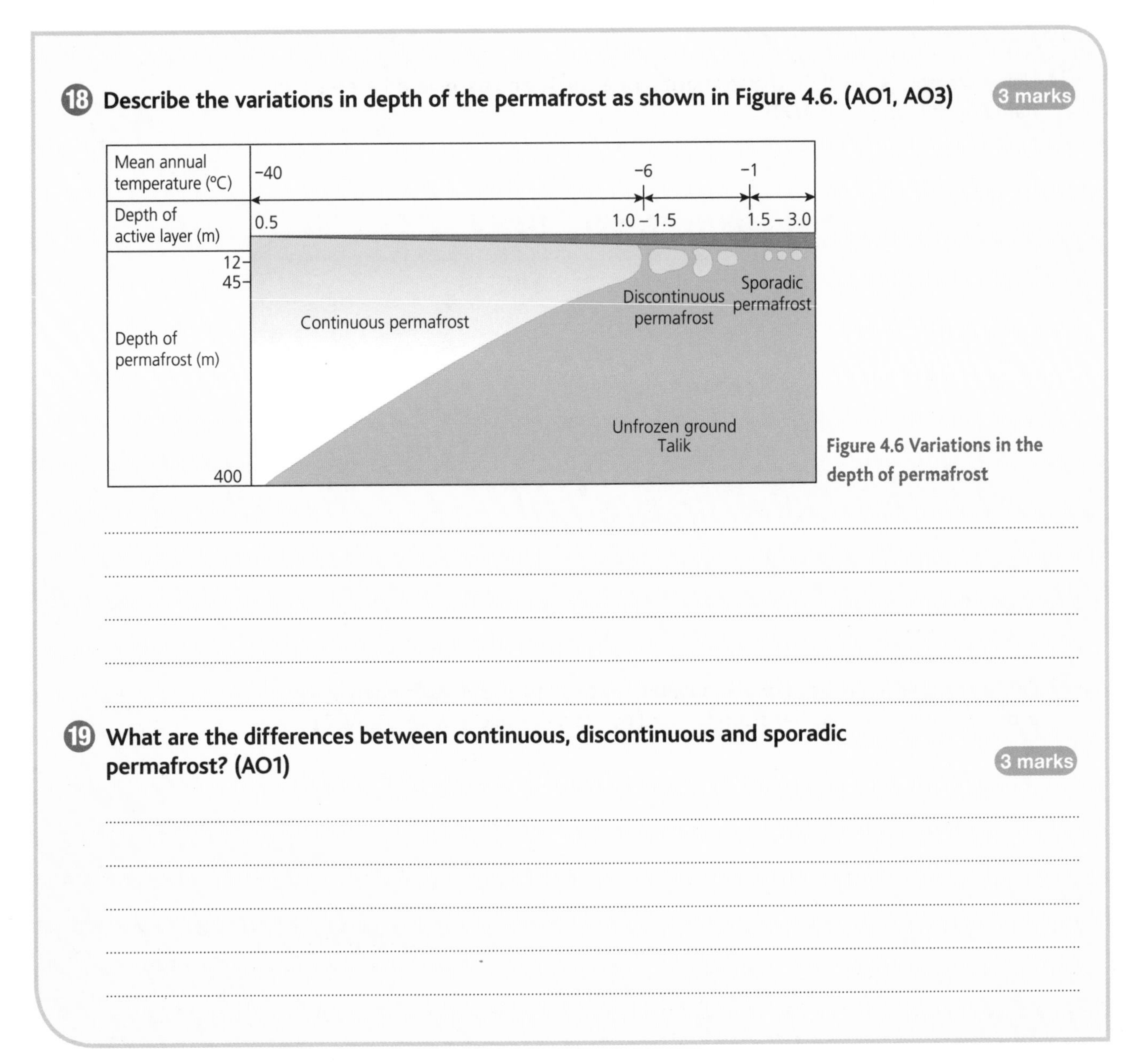

Figure 4.6 Variations in the depth of permafrost

....

....

....

....

....

19 **What are the differences between continuous, discontinuous and sporadic permafrost? (AO1)** 3 marks

....

....

....

....

....

20 **Solifluction is a form of mass movement that occurs in periglacial areas. Explain how the process of solifluction operates and state why it is common in periglacial areas. (AO1, AO2)** 5 marks

....

....

....

....

....

Glaciated landscape development

Glacial landforms

Glaciated landscapes are a combination of landforms that have developed from erosion, deposition and fluvioglacial processes.

21 **Using diagram(s), explain the formation of a corrie and associated arêtes and hanging valleys. (AO1, AO3)** 7 marks

22 **Outline the differences between a valley that has been solely formed by river processes and one that has been formed by glacial processes. (AO1, AO2)** 6 marks

....

....

....

....

....

....

23 **With the help of Figure 4.7 explain how a roche moutonnée is formed. Consider in your answer the roles of erosion processes and regelation flow. (AO1, AO2)** 6 marks

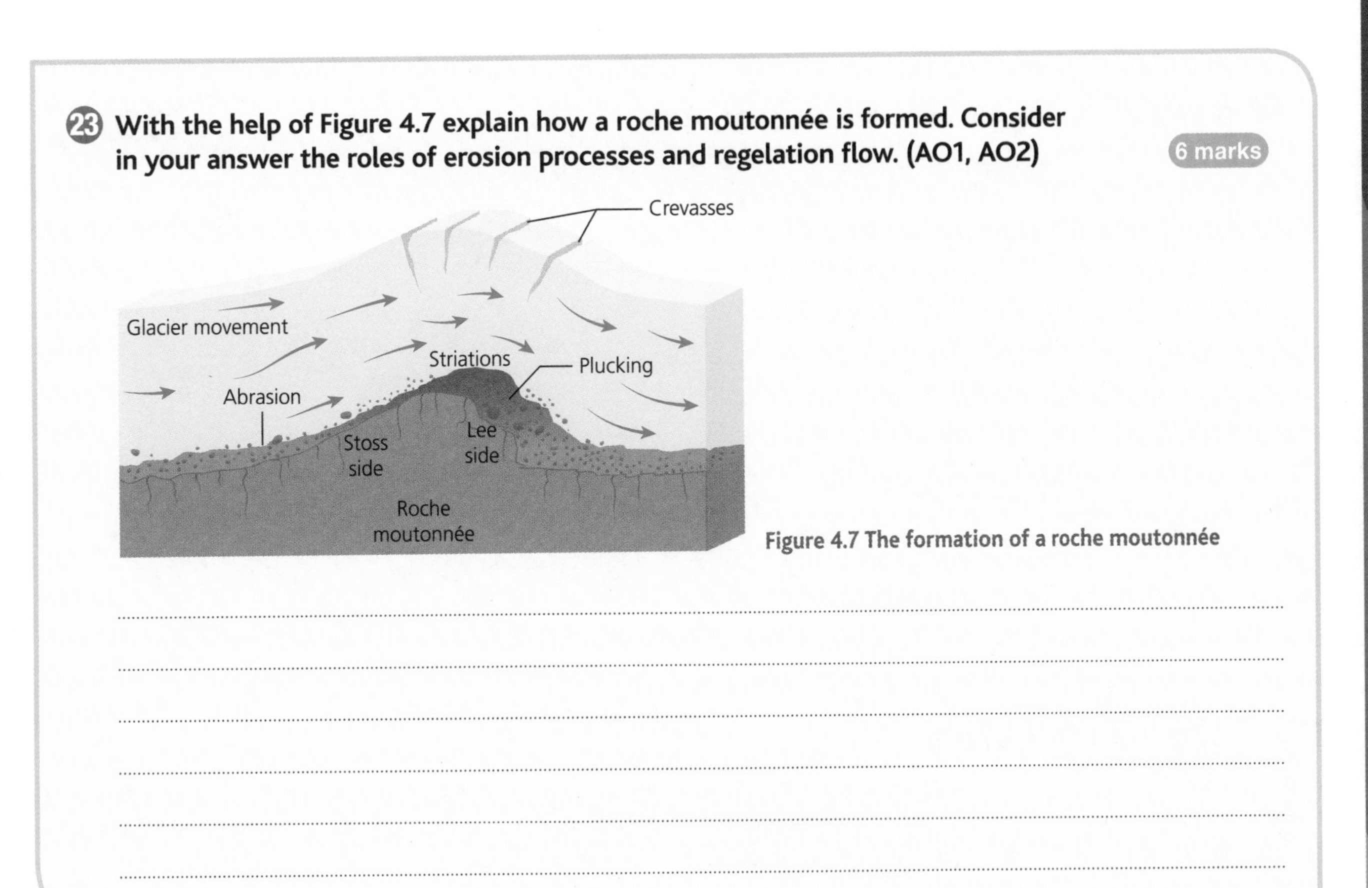

Figure 4.7 The formation of a roche moutonnée

Glacial deposits (i.e. those deposited directly by ice as it melts) include drumlins, erratics, moraines (terminal, recessional, lateral, medial) and till plains.

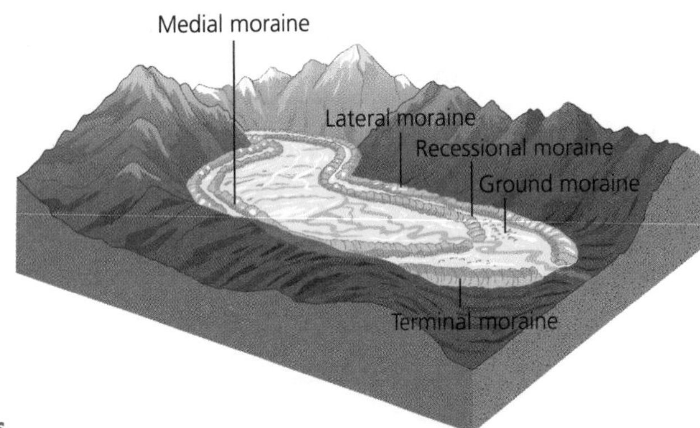

Figure 4.8 The relative positions of glacial moraines

24 **Describe the positions of the various types of moraine and explain how they were formed. (AO1, AO2)** 6 marks

25 Draw a labelled diagram of a drumlin. (AO1, AO3) 4 marks

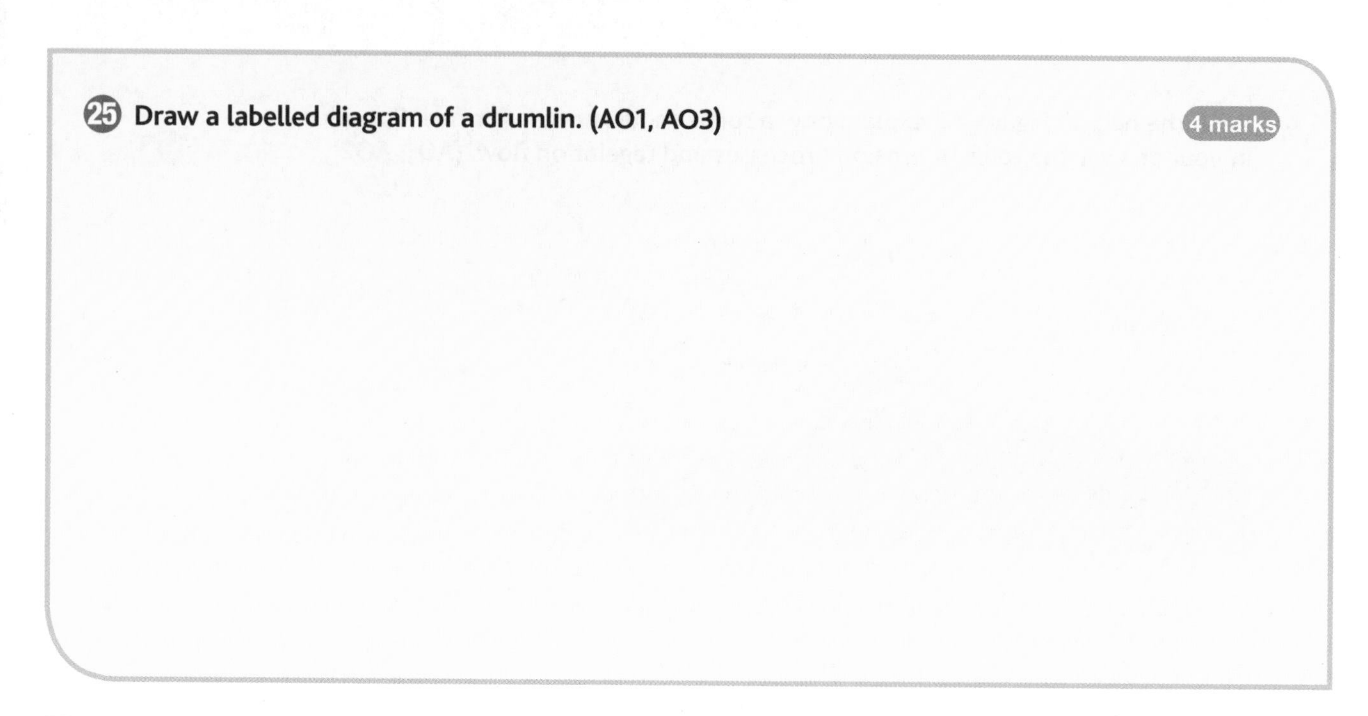

Fluvioglacial landforms

Fluvioglacial landforms are those which have been formed by glacial meltwater. The main characteristic of meltwater streams is that they are high energy, being able to carry a great deal of load. This enables the stream to erode vertically by hydraulic action and abrasion, leading to deep, steep-sided channels. Where the stream energy is lost, deposition occurs, leading to features such as kames, eskers and outwash plains.

26 Using an example, explain how pro-glacial lakes are related to meltwater channels (glacial spillways). (AO1, AO2) 5 marks

....

....

....

....

....

....

....

....

Periglacial landforms

Periglacial landforms develop in areas where there are very cold winters and short cool summers. On low-angled, bare rock surfaces frost action occurs, leading to blockfields. Where there is a slope, scree is formed.

In lowland regions, the permafrost is overlain by a shallow layer of unsorted weathered material called the active layer. The water in the active layer cannot percolate into the frozen permafrost below, leading to saturation. The active layer thaws out when temperatures rise and refreezes in winter (or at night). It is important to note that freezing and thawing occur from the top down. The process of solifluction leads to lobes (see Question 21).

Patterned ground is an umbrella term that covers two completely different landforms that have some similarities in appearance. These are the:

- stone polygon: formed by the process of frost heave (these include circles, nets and stripes)
- ice wedge polygon: formed by the process of ground contraction

27 Outline the process of frost heave and show how it can lead to the formation of stone polygons. (AO1, AO2) **6 marks**

28 Ice wedges and associated polygons only occur where the winter temperatures are extremely low, leading to ground contraction and the appearance of cracks in the surface. Explain how, over time, this leads to ice wedge polygons. (AO1, AO2) **6 marks**

29 Chose one type of pingo (either an open- or a closed-system pingo) and draw a labelled sketch to describe its appearance. Explain how it has been formed. (AO1, AO3) **6 marks**

Thermokarst is a term used to describe a landscape where there has been sporadic melting of the permafrost, leaving a surface covered in small depressions, often filled with water in summer.

30 **Unplanned development in permafrost areas can lead to the formation of thermokarst. Describe the nature of these developments and assess the extent to which it could lead to global climate change. (AO1, AO3)** 10 marks

Exam-style questions (AS)

1 **Outline the ways in which a glacier transports material. (AO1)** 4 3 marks

2 Describe the changing extent of the Glacier Bay glaciers over time as shown in Figure 4.9. What conclusion(s) can be drawn from these data? (AO2, AO3)

7 6 marks

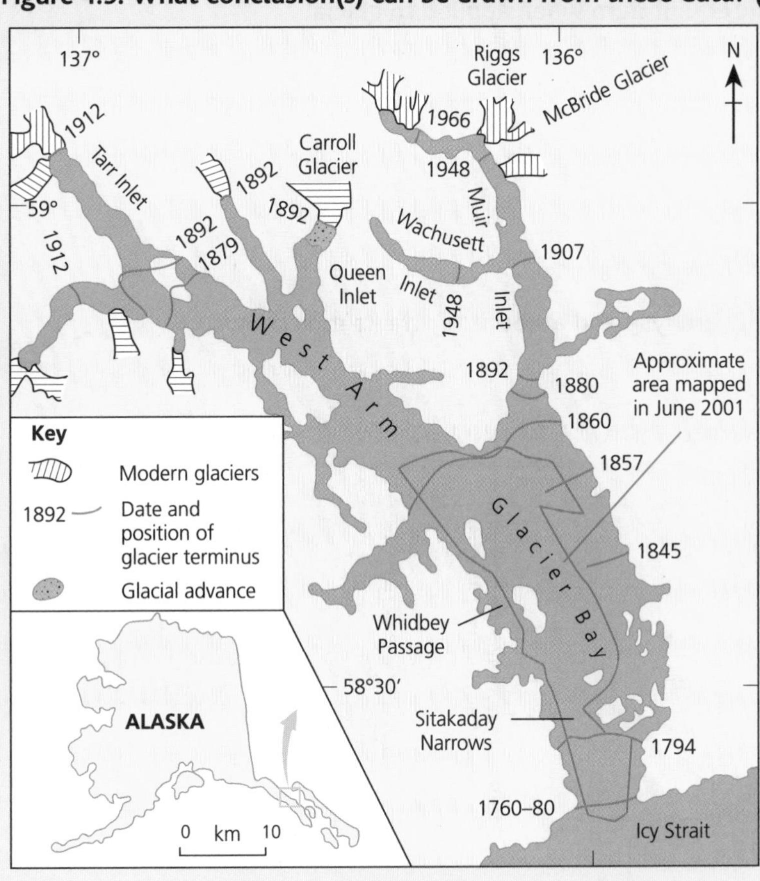

Figure 4.9 The locations of glacial termini in Glacier Bay, Alaska

3 To what extent do periglacial features reflect the global distribution of past and present cold environments? (AO1, AO2)

10 9 marks

Write your answer on a separate sheet of paper.

4 Assess the extent to which fragile cold environments have been affected by globalisation. (AO1, AO2)

22 20 marks

Write your answer on a separate sheet of paper.

Exam-style questions (A-level)

5 **Explain the concept of dynamic equilibrium when applied to glacial systems. (AO2)**

5 4 marks

6 **Using Figures 4.10, 4.11 and 4.12, analyse and account for the trends shown. (AO2, AO3)**

7 6 marks

Information relating to the melting of the Greenland Ice Cap

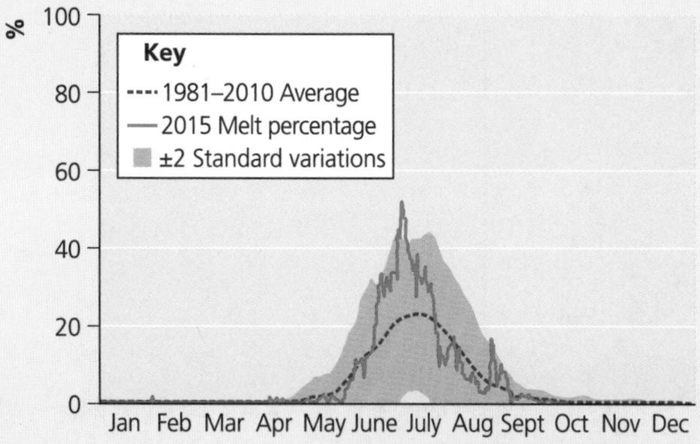

Figure 4.10

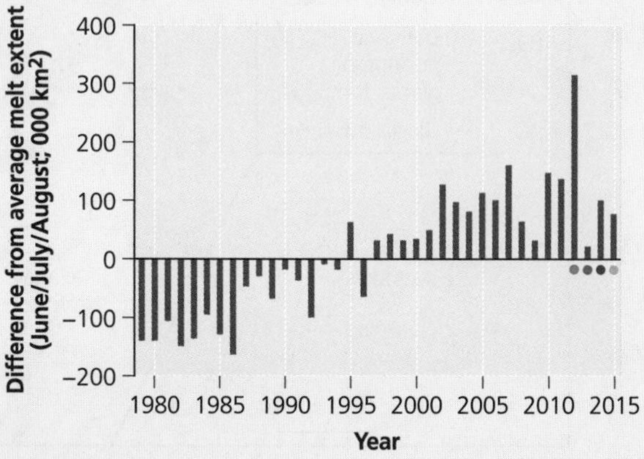

Figure 4.11

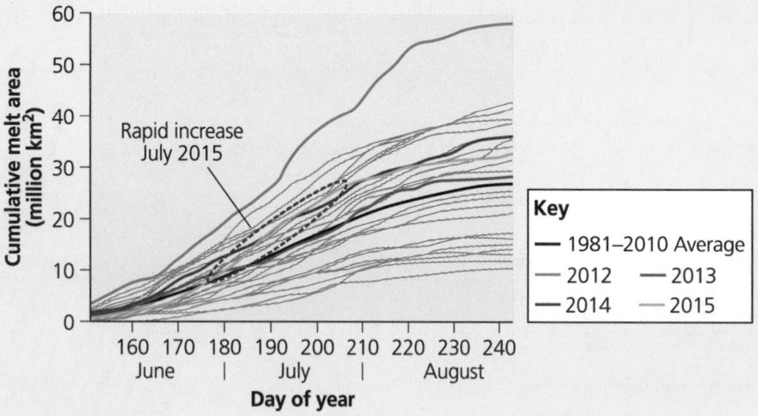

Figure 4.12

7 Assess the relative importance of pre-glacial, glacial and post-glacial processes in creating the landscape shown in Figure 4.13. (AO2, AO3)

7 | 6 marks

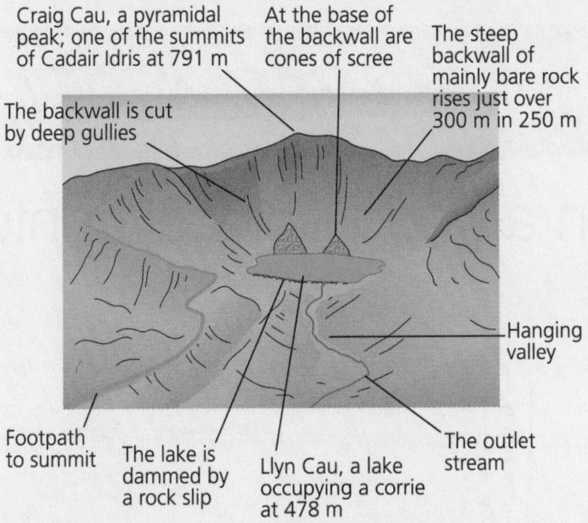

Craig Cau, a pyramidal peak; one of the summits of Cadair Idris at 791 m
At the base of the backwall are cones of scree
The steep backwall of mainly bare rock rises just over 300 m in 250 m
The backwall is cut by deep gullies
Hanging valley
Footpath to summit
The lake is dammed by a rock slip
Llyn Cau, a lake occupying a corrie at 478 m
The outlet stream

Figure 4.13 A field sketch of Llyn Cau, Cadair Idris

8 Using a case study of a contrasting glaciated landscape from beyond the UK, assess the extent to which climate change presents both challenges and opportunities for human occupation. (AO1, AO2)

25 | 20 marks

Make notes below then write your answer on a separate sheet of paper.

Topic 5

Hazards

The concept of hazard in a geographical context

Modern ideas see hazards as the outcome of the interaction between human use systems (like land use) and natural event systems (the natural environmental processes which give rise to hazards). This interaction promotes actual hazard events which we perceive and then respond to. The way we react can in turn modify the human use system (for example by changing land use), the natural events system (for example by changing the magnitude/frequency relationship for river flooding), or both.

The Park model of human responses to a hazard sketches the phases following a hazard event.

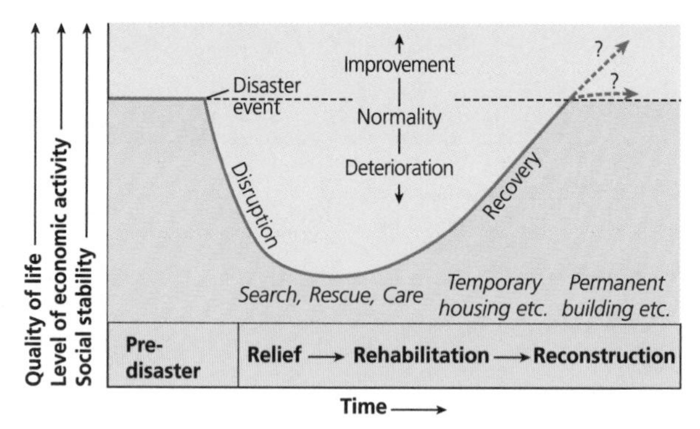

Figure 5.1 The Park model of human responses to a hazard

1 Outline the activities that might take place during the relief phase. (AO1, AO2) 6 marks

....

....

....

....

....

....

....

....

2 What are the differences between the rehabilitation phase and the reconstruction phase? (AO1, AO2) 6 marks

....

....

....

....

....

....

....

....

....

3 **Outline two characteristic human responses to hazards using examples of where these types of responses can be found. (AO1, AO2)** 6 marks

....

....

....

....

....

....

....

....

4 **Using Figure 5.2 and examples from your studies, explain the extent to which the time interval between disasters impacts on an area's response to those disasters. (AO1, AO2)** 10 marks

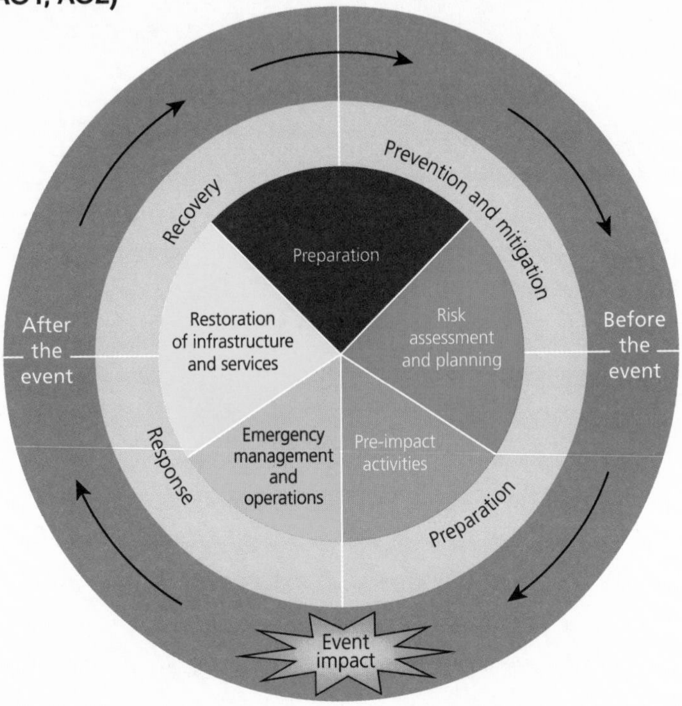

Figure 5.2 The hazard management cycle

....

....

....

....

....

....

....

....

....

....

....

Plate tectonics

Plate tectonics is the theory that the Earth's outer shell (the crust or lithosphere) is divided into several plates that glide over the rocky inner layer (the mantle) above the core. The plates act like a hard and rigid shell compared to the mantle. Developed from the 1950s through to the 1970s, plate tectonics is the modern version of the theory of continental drift, a theory first proposed by Alfred Wegener in 1912.

The crust of the Earth is divided into rigid plates that vary in shape and size and move relative to one another over the globe. There are nine major plates: the Eurasian, African, South American, North American, Nazca, Antarctic, Pacific, Juan De Fuca and Indian–Australian.

Most of the edges of these plates are geologically active.

5 **Describe the main features (location, temperature, chemistry etc.) of the following: (AO1)**

15 marks

a **The oceanic crust**

....

....

....

b **The continental crust**

....

....

....

c **The asthenosphere**

....

....

....

d **The mantle**

....

....

....

e **The core**

....

....

....

6 **To what extent does the mantle convection hypothesis explain plate movements at destructive boundaries and constructive plate margins? (AO1, AO2)**

8 marks

....

....

....

....

....

....

7 Describe the differences between the ridge push hypothesis and the slab pull hypothesis. (AO1) 5 marks

....
....
....
....
....
....
....
....

Constructive plate boundaries occur where plates move away from each other and fresh magma wells up to fill the gap. This creates new crust as it cools and solidifies. Figure 5.3 shows how these boundaries evolve from a bulge in the crust underneath upwelling magma to a continental rift valley (e.g. the Great African Rift Valley), to a linear sea (e.g. the Red Sea) and finally to an ocean.

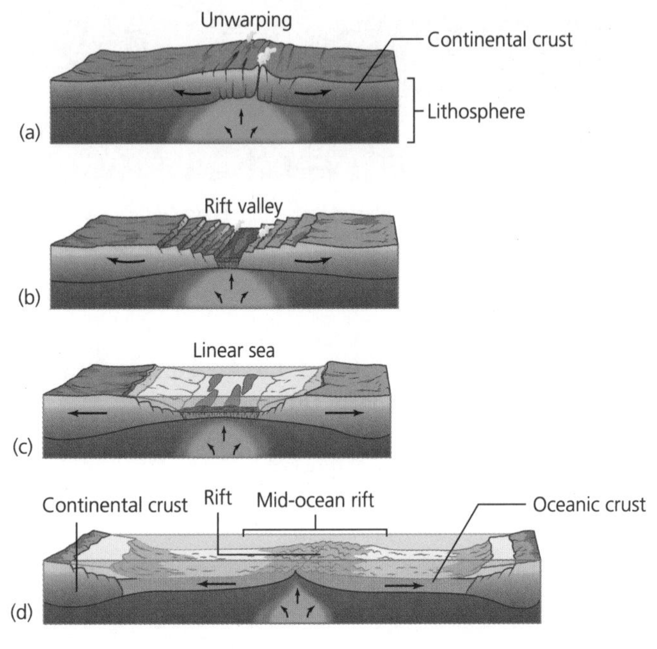

Figure 5.3 The evolution of a constructive plate margin

8 Use plate tectonic theory to account for the evolution of oceans as shown in Figure 5.3. (AO1, AO2) 6 marks

....
....
....
....
....
....
....
....
....

9 **The magma and lavas produced at constructive plate margins are low in silica content. To what extent does this affect the nature of the volcanic eruptions found at this type of boundary? (AO1, AO2)** 4 marks

....

....

....

....

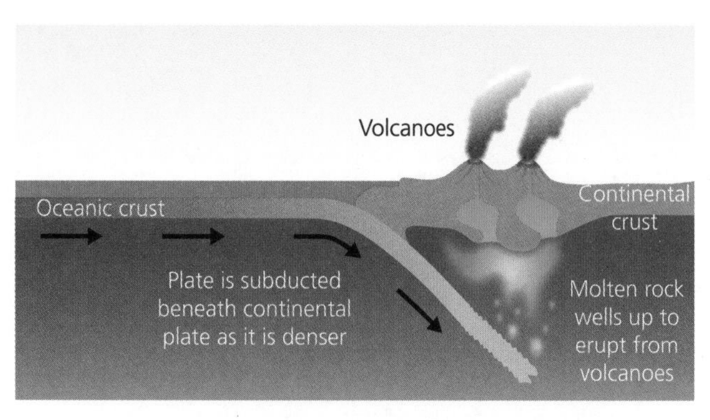

Figure 5.4 An ocean/continent destructive plate boundary

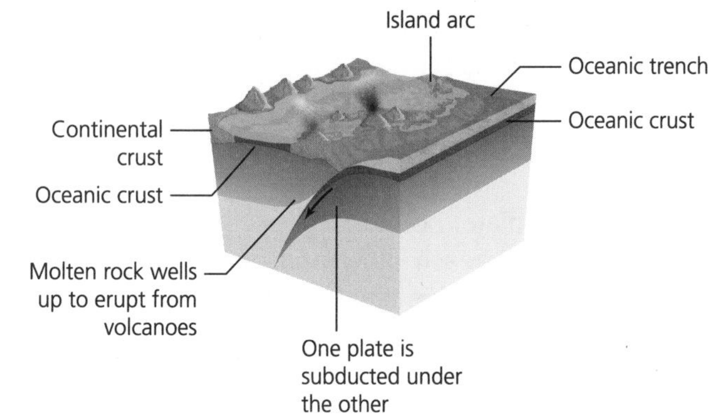

Figure 5.5 An ocean/ocean destructive plate boundary (an island arc)

10 **Study Figures 5.4 and 5.5. Account for the fact that earthquakes occur at these two types of boundary. (AO1, AO2)** 4 marks

....

....

....

....

....

....

11 **Describe the nature of the volcanic eruptions at both types of boundaries shown in Figures 5.4 and 5.5. (AO1, AO2)** 6 marks

....

....

....

....

....

....

....

....

....

12 **Explain why collision boundaries such as that between the Indo/Australian plate and the Eurasian plate produce many earthquakes. (AO1, AO2)** 4 marks

....

....

....

....

....

....

13 **Explain why earthquakes at conservative plate boundaries are potentially so destructive. (AO1, AO2)** 4 marks

....

....

....

....

....

....

14 **Using Figure 5.6 explain how the moving Pacific plate and the magma plume work together to form a chain of islands. (AO1, AO2)** 6 marks

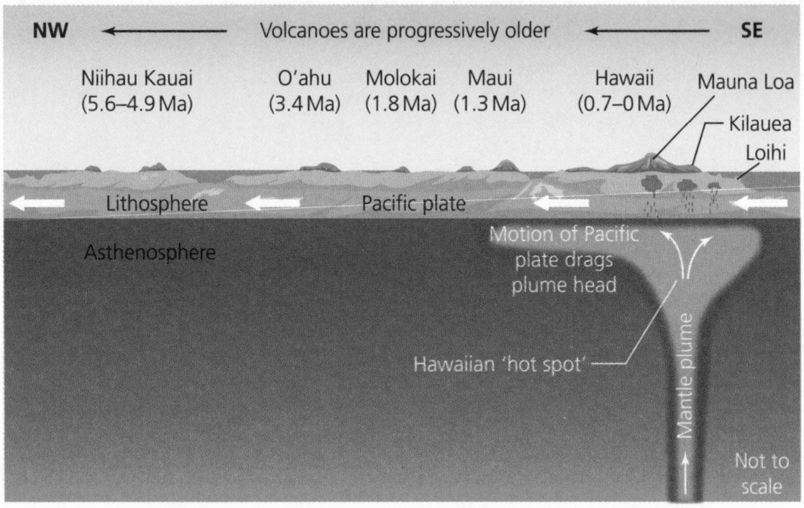

Figure 5.6 A chain of 'hot-spot' volcanoes in the Hawaiian Islands

....

....

....

....

....

....

....

....

....

Volcanic hazards

A volcanic hazard refers to any potentially dangerous volcanic process (e.g. lava flows, pyroclastic flows, ash). A volcanic risk is any potential loss or damage as a result of the volcanic hazard that might be incurred by persons, property etc. or which negatively impacts the productive capacity/sustainability of a population.

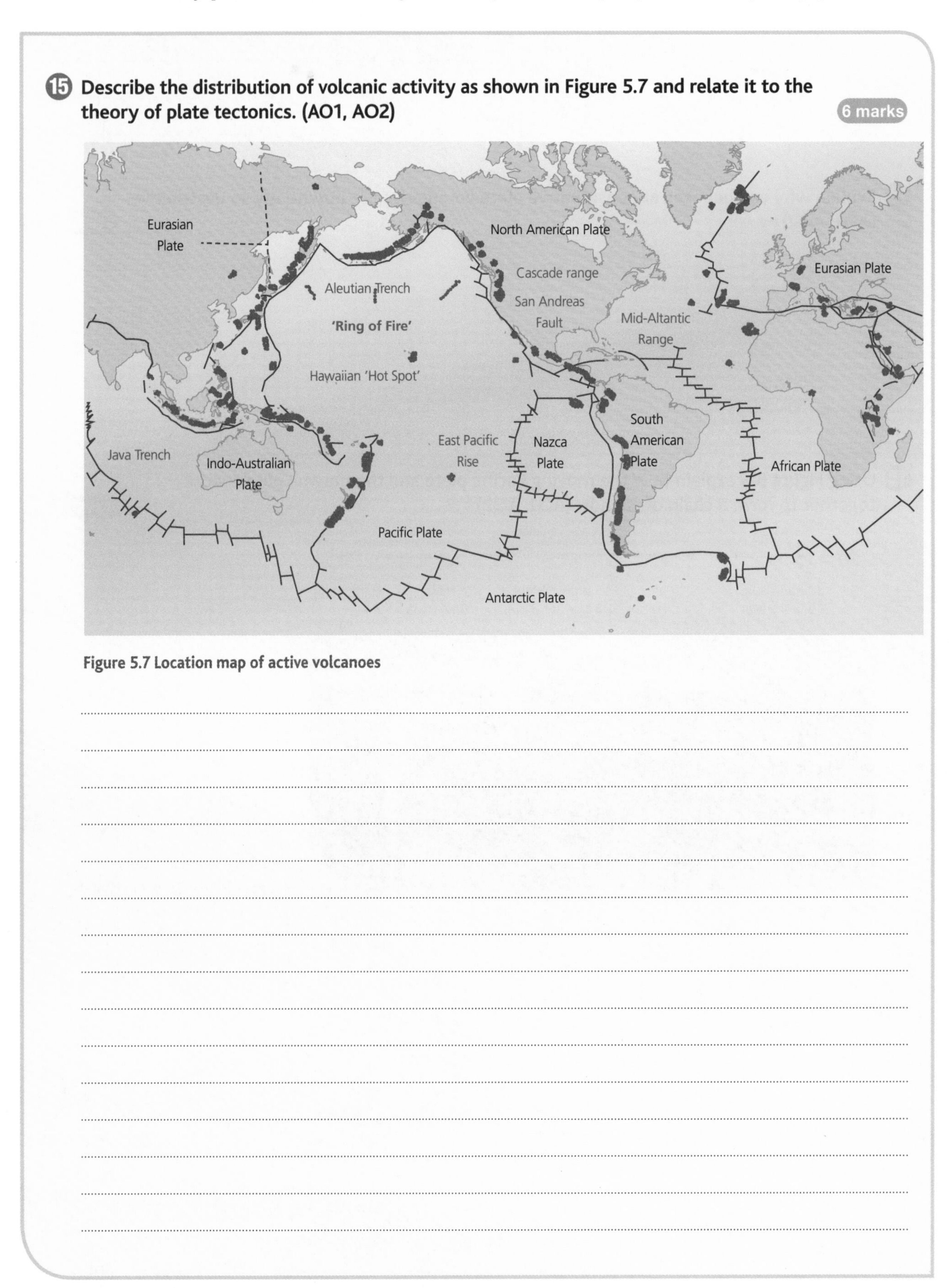

15 Describe the distribution of volcanic activity as shown in Figure 5.7 and relate it to the theory of plate tectonics. (AO1, AO2) 6 marks

Figure 5.7 Location map of active volcanoes

16 Choose two of the volcanic hazards shown in Figure 5.8 and, using examples, explain the cause and describe the effects of the named hazards. (AO1, AO2) 8 marks

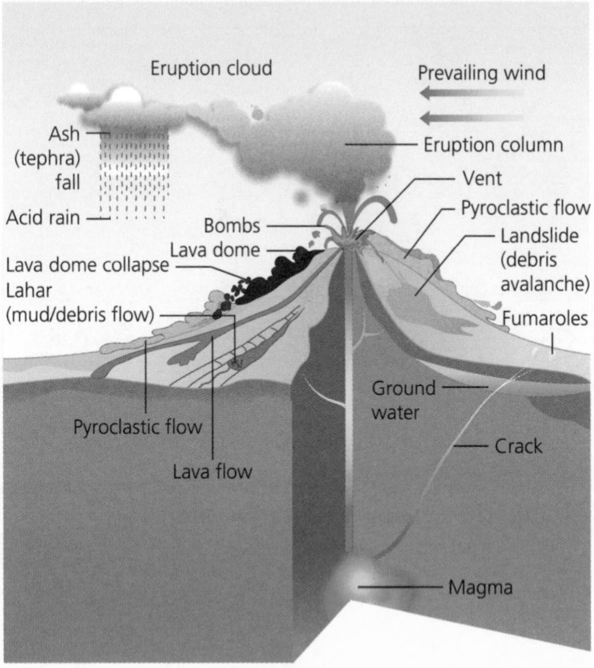

Figure 5.8 A simplified diagram showing some of the most common forms of volcanic hazard

....

....

....

....

....

....

....

....

....

....

....

....

Seismic hazards

Most of the seismic hazards to people come from human-made structures and the shaking they receive from earthquakes. The real dangers to people are being crushed in a collapsing building, drowning in a flood caused by a broken dam or levee, getting buried under a landslide, or being burned in a fire.

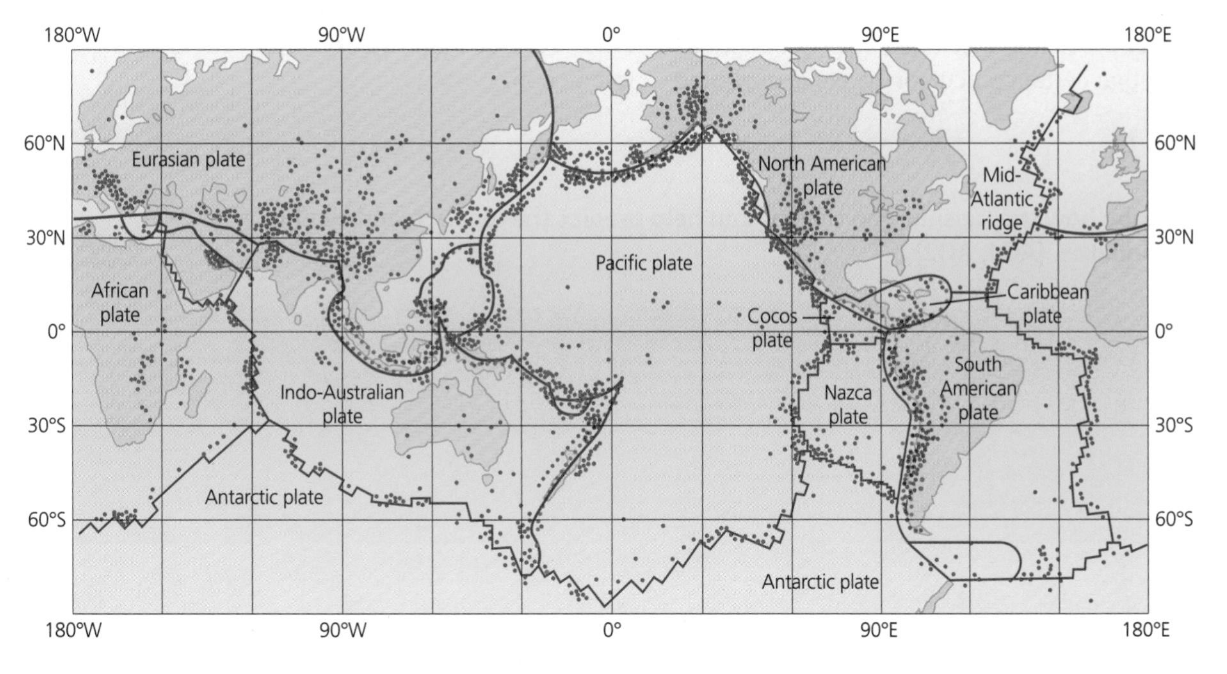

Figure 5.9 Earthquake locations for events between 1965 and 1995. The red dots are shallow earthquakes, the green are intermediate depth, and the purple are deep

17 **To what extent do earthquakes in general, and their depth in particular, conform to what we know about tectonic plate boundaries? (AO1, AO2)** 8 marks

....

....

....

....

....

....

....

....

....

18 **Earthquake hazards include earthquakes themselves, shockwaves, tsunamis, liquefaction and landslides. Using examples, explain the cause and describe the effects of two named hazards. (AO1, AO2)** 8 marks

....

....

....

....

....

....

....

....

Although scientists know most of the global locations where earthquakes are likely to occur, they still have great difficulty predicting when they may occur. It has been noticed that certain precursor events (e.g. ground uplift, emission of radon gas etc.) can be monitored and observed changes can help in short-term prediction. The 'seismic gap theory' is used for longer-term prediction.

19 **Describe how the 'seismic gap theory' can help predict the location and timing of earthquakes. (AO1, AO2)** 6 marks

....

....

....

....

....

....

....

....

Storm hazards

A tropical storm (or cyclone) is the generic term for a low-pressure system over tropical or subtropical waters, with organised convection (i.e. thunderstorm activity) and winds at low levels circulating either anticlockwise (in the northern hemisphere) or clockwise (in the southern hemisphere). The whole storm system may be 8,000 m to 9,500 m high and 200 to 700 km wide, although sometimes can be even bigger. It typically moves forward at speeds of 16–20 km/h but can travel as fast as 60 km/h.

20 With the help of Figure 5.10, describe the structure of a typical tropical revolving storm. (AO1) 6 marks

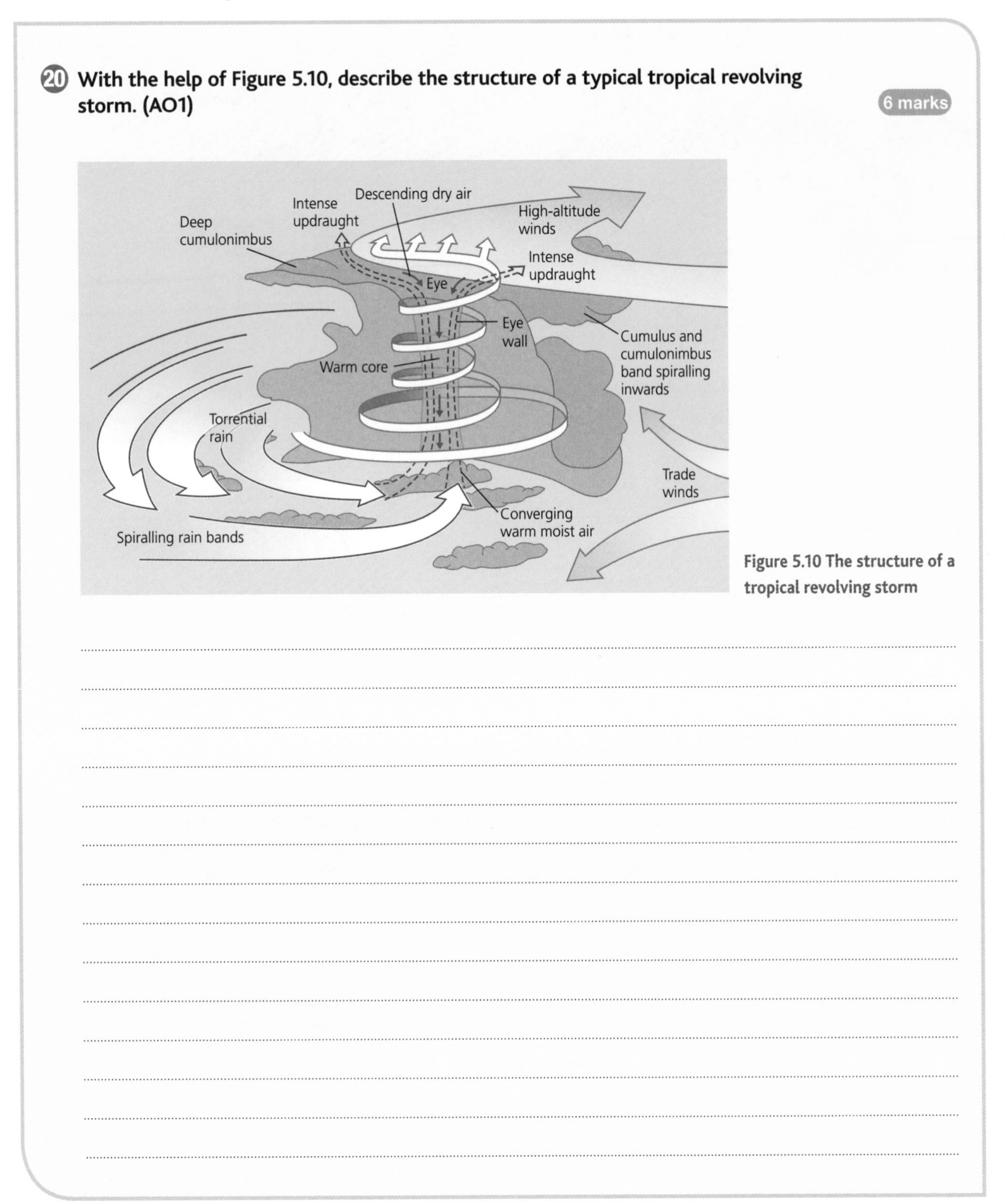

Figure 5.10 The structure of a tropical revolving storm

Tropical storms require a certain set of environmental conditions in order to develop. Once they have been triggered, they move westwards and northwards (southwards in the southern hemisphere) until they come under the influence of westerly winds. They then start to reverse their direction into an easterly path.

21 Using Figure 5.11, describe and account for the global distribution of tropical storms and the time of their occurrence. (AO1, AO2, AO3) 8 marks

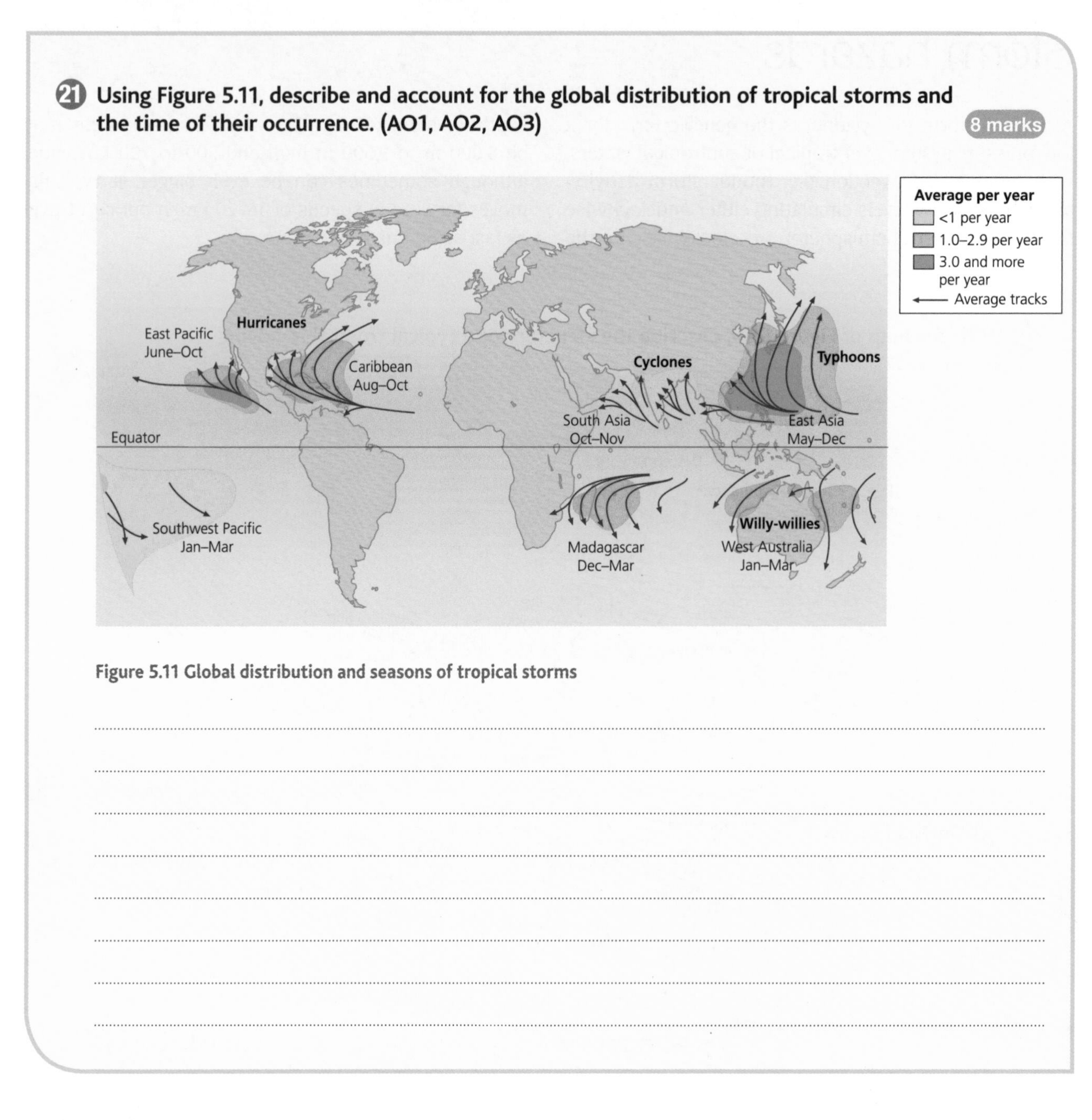

Figure 5.11 Global distribution and seasons of tropical storms

Tropical storms pose threats to coastal communities in the form of high winds, storm surges, coastal flooding and landslides. Their impact is huge. Between 1980 and 2009, 466 million people were affected, including 412,644 deaths and 290,654 injuries. The primary cause of cyclone-related mortality in both developed and less developed countries was storm surge drowning.

22 Why might a decreased proportion of deaths and injuries be observed in the aftermath of cyclones as a result of improved early warning systems and evacuation? (AO1) 4 marks

23 **To what extent do the impacts of tropical storms and the human responses depend on both the physical nature of the environment as well as the level of economic development? (AO1, AO2)** 20 marks

Write your answer on a separate sheet of paper.

Fires in nature

24 **Complete Table 5.1. (AO1, AO2)** 8 marks

Table 5.1 Conditions favouring wildfires

Factor	Impact on wildfire
Vegetation type	
Fuel characteristics	
Climate	
Recent weather conditions	
Fire behaviour	

25 **Outline how wildfires can be started. (AO1)** 3 marks

26 **For a recent wildfire event you have studied, assess the extent to which the human responses to that event were able to reduce the impact of the fire. (AO1, AO2)** 10 marks

Exam-style questions (AS)

1 Outline how risk management can reduce the impacts of wildfires. (AO1)

....

....

....

....

2 The United Nations office for Disaster Reduction has produced statistics regarding the number of natural disasters and the total costs of the damage incurred.

Table 5.2 shows the figures for the top ten countries with most disasters between 2005 and 2014.

Table 5.2

Country	Number of natural disasters	Rank	Total damage ($ billion)	Rank	*d*	*d*²
China	286	1	265	2	−1	1
USA	212	2	443	1	+1	1
Philippines	181	3	16	7	−4	16
India	167	4	47	4	0	0
Indonesia	141	5	11	8	−3	9
Vietnam	73	6	7	9	−3	9
Afghanistan	72	7	0.16	10	...	...
Mexico	64	8	26	5	3	9
Japan	62	9	239	3	...	...
Pakistan	59	10	25	6	4	16

Calculate the Spearman's rank correlation coefficient for the two sets of data by completing Table 5.2 and using the formula:

$$R_s = 1 - \frac{6 \sum d^2}{n^3 - n}$$

Where:

R_s is the Spearman's rank correlation coefficient

n is the number of pairs of variables

$\sum d^2$ is the sum of the differences in rank squared.

Critical values for Spearman's rank where n = 10:

n	Significance level	
	0.05	0.01
10	+/− 0.564	+/− 0.746

Complete Table 5.2 and interpret your Spearman's rank result using the critical values above. (AO3)

6 marks

....

....

....

....

....

3 **Analyse the extent to which the impacts of volcanic hazards depend on the nature of the vulcanicity. (AO1, AO2)** 10 **9 marks**

4 **Assess the extent to which the Park model of human responses applies to TWO or more recent hazard events you have studied. (AO1, AO2)** 22 **20 marks**

Make notes below and then write your answer as a separate sheet of paper.

Exam-style questions (A-level)

5 **Study Figure 5.12 and analyse the possible climatic variables that have an effect on the occurrence and length of the fire season in the western USA. (AO2, AO3)** 7 — 6 marks

(a) Western US forest wildfires and spring–summer temperatures

(b) Timing of spring snowmelt

(c) Fire season length

Figure 5.12 Annual frequency of large (> 400 ha) western US forest wildfires (bars) and mean March–August temperatures (a); timing of spring snowmelt for western USA (b) and fire season length (c)

6 **To what extent do you agree that risk management has had an effect on the impacts of a recent volcanic event you have studied? (AO1, AO2)** 11 — 9 marks

7 **Outline the theory of plate tectonics and assess the extent to which the position of young fold mountains, rift valleys, ocean ridges, volcanoes, deep sea trenches and island arcs support that theory. (AO1, AO2)**

11 | 9 marks

8 **Using an example of a multi-hazardous environment beyond the UK, illustrate and analyse the nature of the hazards of that environment and the social, economic and environmental risks presented. To what extent do human qualities and responses contribute to its continuing human occupation? (AO1, AO2)**

25 | 20 marks

Make notes below and then write your answer on a separate sheet of paper.

Topic 6

Ecosystems under stress

Ecosystems and sustainability

Biodiversity, which is short for **biological diversity**, is the term used to describe the whole variety of life on Earth. It encompasses the diversity of all living things, from human beings to microorganisms, the diversity of all the habitats in which they live and the genetic diversity of individuals within a species. It can be measured in a variety of ways including:

- indicator species
- species richness
- the Living Planet Index (LPI)

1 Describe the three ways that can be used to measure biodiversity, giving one advantage and one disadvantage of each. (AO1) 9 marks

2 Describe the changes in the Living Planet Index as shown in Figure 6.1. (AO2, AO3) 2 marks

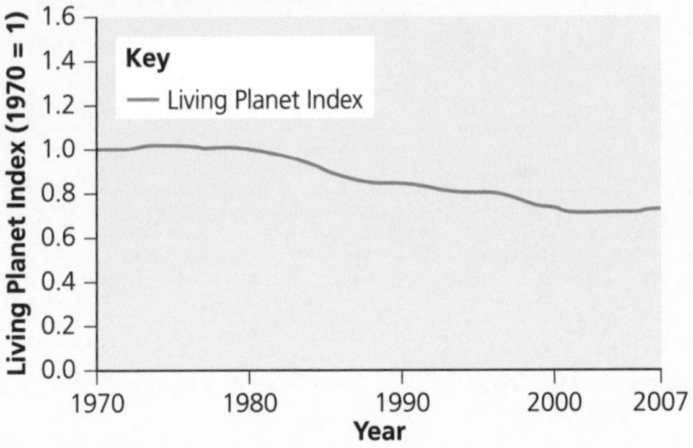

Figure 6.1 The Living Planet Index, 1970–2007

3 **Complete Table 6.1 by giving named examples of species that have declined due to the named human activity. (AO1, AO2)** 10 marks

Table 6.1 Some of the main causes of the decrease in biodiversity

Pressure	Example(s) of species that has declined
Effects of human activity on biodiversity	
Habitat loss, alteration and fragmentation	
Overexploitation of wild species	
Pollution	
Climate change	
Invasive species	

Ecosystem services are the benefits that people obtain from ecosystems. The Millennium Ecosystem Assessment (MEA) analysed 24 ecosystem services, and found that 15 were being degraded or used unsustainably. The decline in services affects the world's disadvantaged people most strongly, impedes sustainable development globally and, in developing countries, represents a considerable barrier to achieving the UN's Millennium Development Goals of reducing poverty and hunger.

4 **Outline the benefits of having healthy biodiversity in each of the following ecosystem services. (AO1, AO2)** 9 marks

- **Provisioning service**

....

....

....

....

- **Environmental regulation**

....

....

....

....

- **Cultural service**

....

....

....

....

Ecosystems and processes

The nature of ecosystems

An ecosystem is a community of living and non-living things that work together. Each ecosystem has two main components:

- Abiotic components are all of the non-living things in an ecosystem.
- Biotic components are the living organisms including plants, animals and microorganisms (bacteria and fungi) that are present in an ecosystem.

The trophic level of an organism is the position it occupies in a food chain.

5 Describe the general structure of an ecosystem. (AO1) 8 marks

....

....

....

....

....

....

....

....

....

....

....

....

....

....

....

....

....

6 Using examples, explain the concept of a food chain. (AO1, AO2) 4 marks

....

....

....

....

....

....

....

....

....

7 Explain why the trophic levels are shown as a pyramid as in Figure 6.2. (AO1, AO2) 4 marks

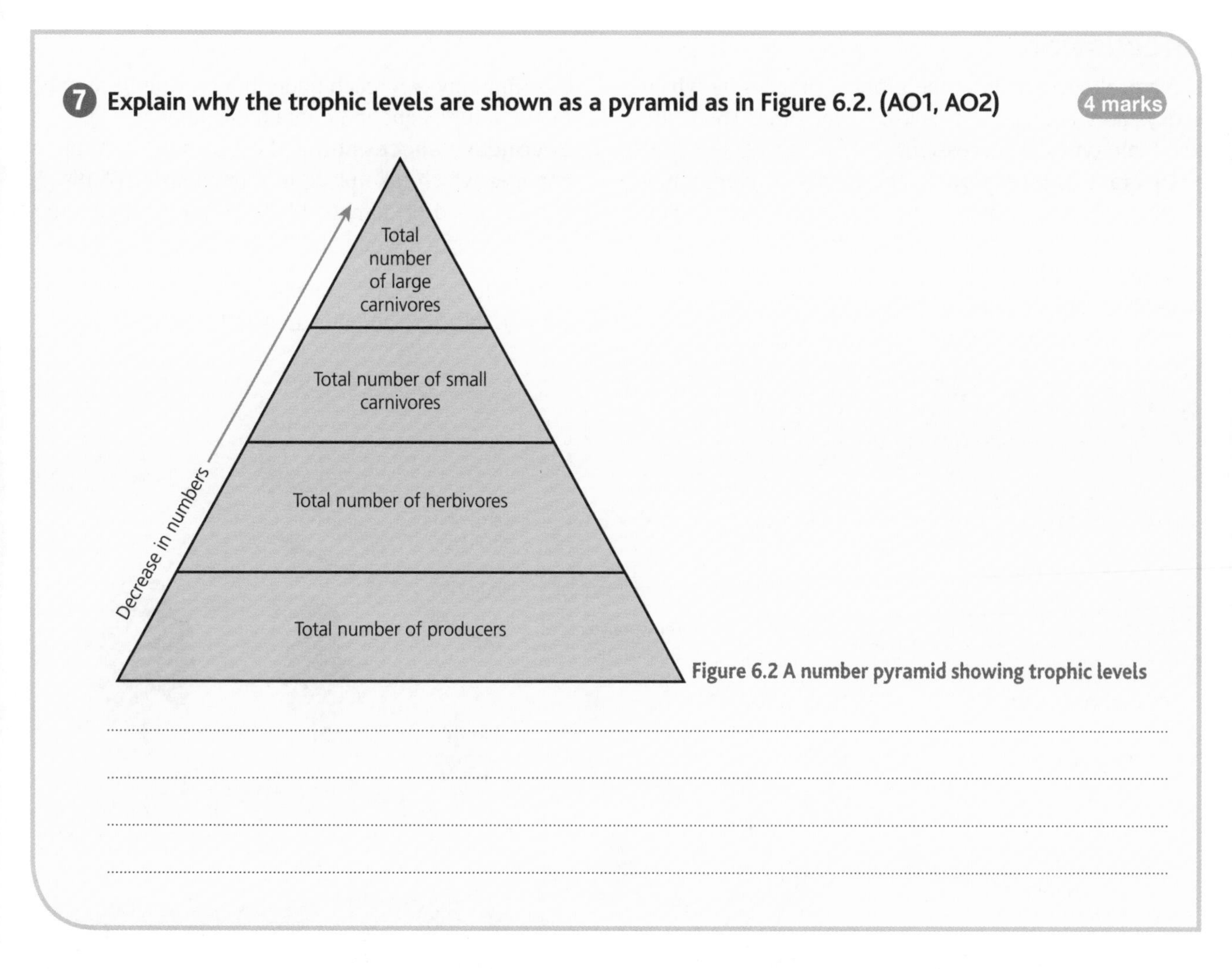

Figure 6.2 A number pyramid showing trophic levels

Most food chains are interconnected. Animals typically consume a varied diet and, in turn, serve as food for a variety of other creatures that prey on them. These interconnections create food webs.

8 Construct a food web diagram for a temperate deciduous woodland biome typical of the British Isles. (AO1, AO2, AO3) 

Succession

Ecological succession is the gradual process by which ecosystems change and develop over time. There are two main types of succession:

- **Primary succession** is the series of community changes (seres) which occur in an entirely new habitat that has never been colonised before, for example a recent lava flow. Succession continues until it reaches climatic climax. This is the final seral stage. It represents the maximum possible development that a community can reach under the prevailing climatic (temperature, light and rainfall) conditions.
- **Secondary succession** is the series of community changes which take place in a previously colonised, but disturbed or damaged habitat, for example after felling trees in a woodland, land clearance or a fire.

You need to know and understand the processes that occur in a lithosere and a hydrosere in the British Isles.

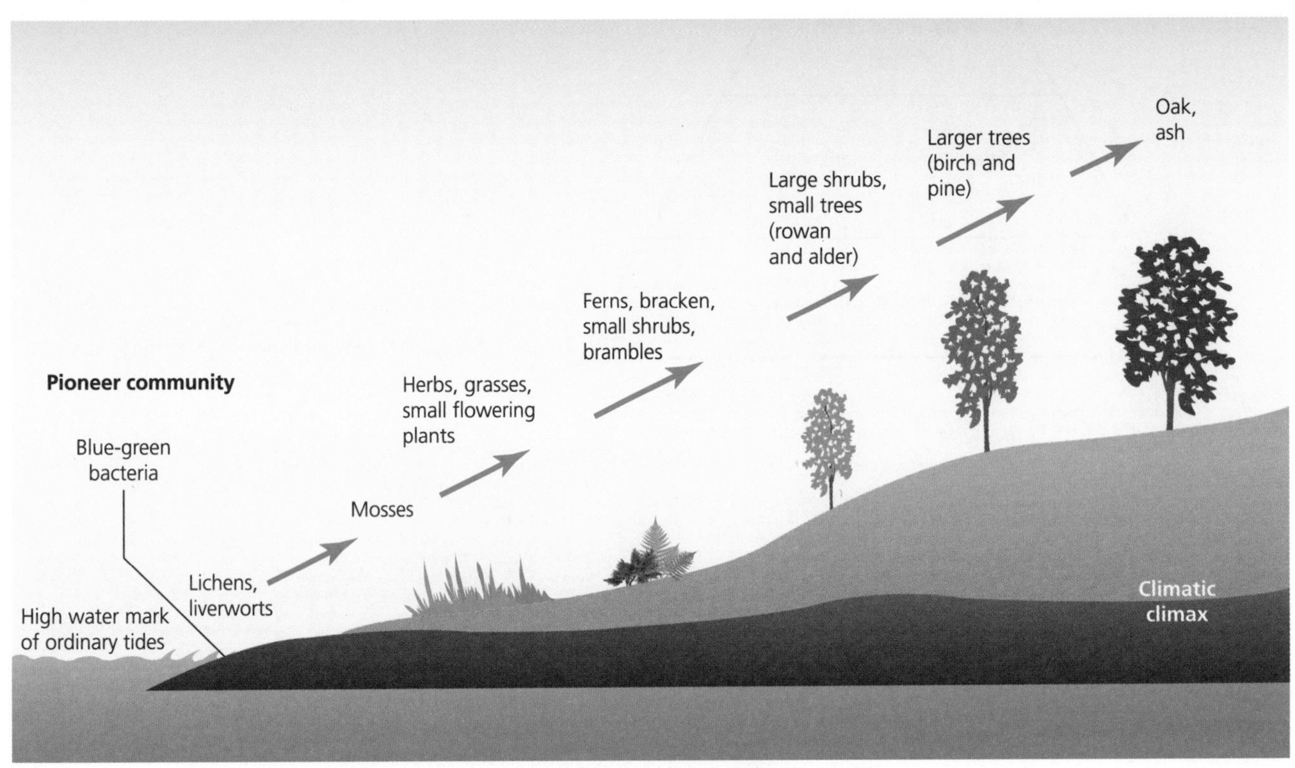

Figure 6.3 The development of a lithosere on a raised beach in the British Isles

9 **Using Figure 6.3 analyse the changes that take place during the development of a lithosere on a raised beach in the British Isles. (AO1, AO2, AO3)** **9 marks**

....

....

....

....

....

....

....

....

....

....

....

....

10 **Describe and explain the stages and processes that occur as a pond (e.g. a kettle-hole lake) evolves from pond to deciduous woodland. (AO1, AO2, AO3)** 9 marks

....

....

....

....

....

....

....

....

Nutrients are the chemical elements and compounds needed for organisms to grow and function. Nutrients are stored in three compartments within an ecosystem. They are:

- soil: a mixture of weathered rock, air, water and decomposed organic matter on the surface of the Earth
- litter: the amount of dead organic matter on top of soil
- biomass: the total of plant and animal life in an ecosystem

These nutrients are cycled from one store to another, as shown in Figure 6.4.

11 **Annotate the model of the mineral nutrient cycle (Figure 6.4) with the following labels: (AO1, AO3)** 10 marks

Biomass
Soil
Litter
Loss by leaching
Loss in runoff
Uptake by plants
Fallout as tissues die
Release as litter decomposes
Input dissolved in rainfall
Input from weathered rock

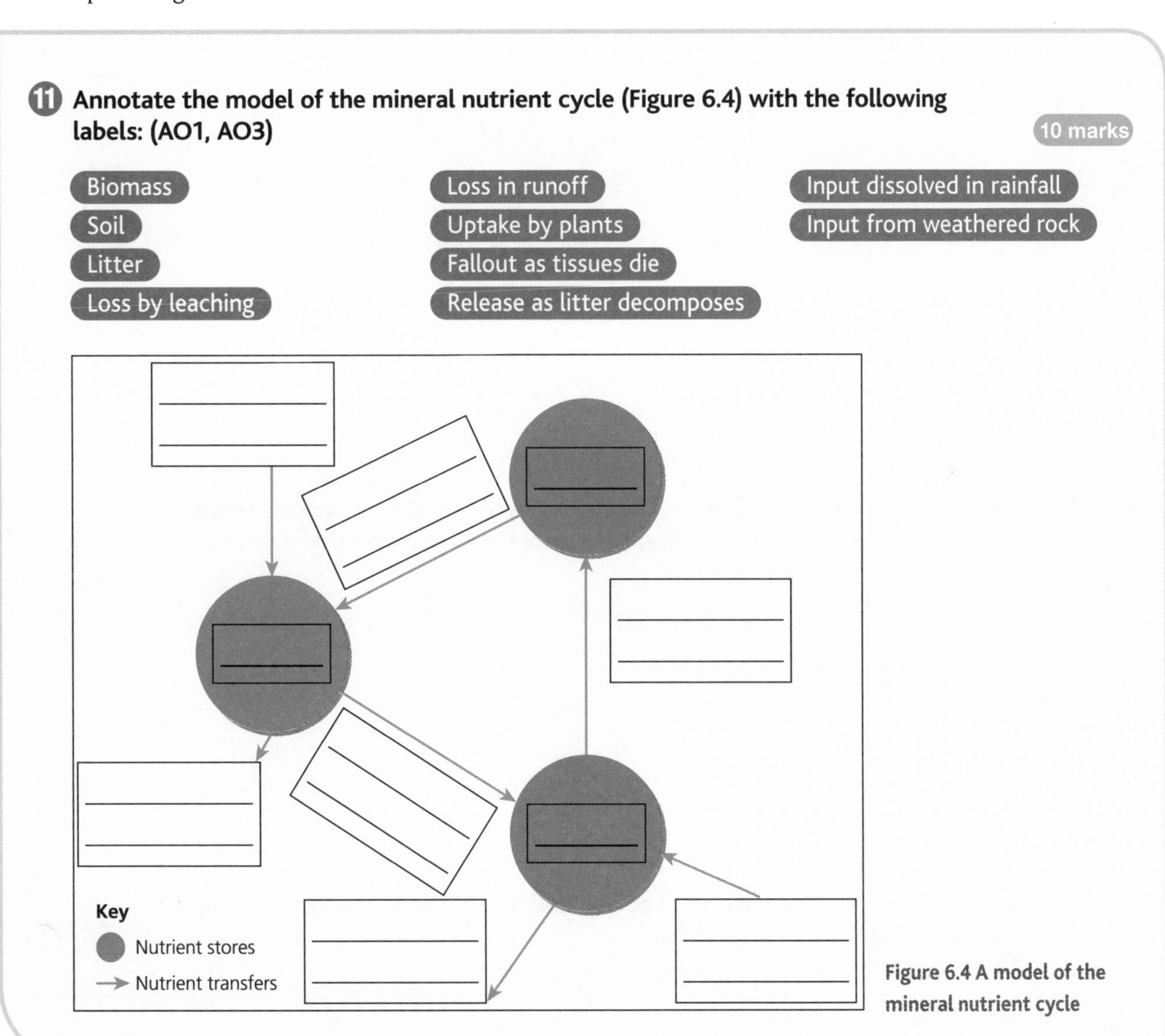

Figure 6.4 A model of the mineral nutrient cycle

Changing ecosystems

Climate is an important environmental influence on ecosystems. Climate changes and the impacts of climate change affect ecosystems in a variety of ways. Climate not only affects ecosystems and species directly, it also interacts with other human stressors such as development. For instance, climate change may exacerbate the stress that land development places on fragile coastal areas.

12 **Outline two ways in which climate change has affected the timing of seasonal life-cycle events. (AO1, AO2)** 4 marks

....

....

....

....

....

13 **Outline two examples where climate change has affected the habitat ranges of species. (AO1, AO2)** 4 marks

....

....

....

....

....

....

14 **Describe two examples where climate change may disrupt food webs. (AO1, AO2)** 4 marks

....

....

....

....

....

....

15 **Name an example of how climate change has encouraged conditions where parasites or diseases have thrived. Explain how they have affected the provision of ecosystem services. (AO1, AO2)** 4 marks

....

....

....

....

....

....

16 **Name an example of a species that has become extinct or is on the verge of becoming extinct because of climate change. (AO1)** 1 mark

....

Biomes

A biome is a large community of plants and animals that occupies a distinct region defined by its climate and dominant vegetation. You must know details of tropical rainforest and savanna grasslands.

17 Describe the global distribution of:

a tropical rainforest (AO1) 3 marks

....

....

....

....

b savanna grassland (AO1) 3 marks

....

....

....

....

The tropical rainforest

18 Describe a typical rainforest climate. (AO1, AO2) 3 marks

....

....

....

....

19 The typical soil of the rainforest is a latosol. Draw an annotated soil profile of a latosol showing the main characteristics. (AO1, AO3) 4 marks

20 **Study Figure 6.5. Describe and explain the main features of the mineral nutrient cycle of a rainforest. (AO2, AO3)** 4 marks

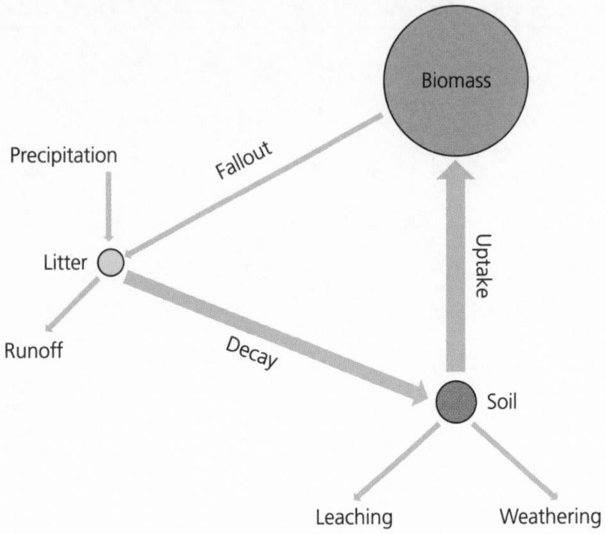

Figure 6.5 The mineral nutrient cycle for a tropical rainforest

....

....

....

....

....

21 **Describe the ways in which the vegetation has developed and adapted to the physical conditions of the rainforest. (AO1, AO2)** 3 marks

....

....

....

....

....

22 **Using examples, outline some development issues found within the tropical rainforest biome that are associated with the following changes.**

For each one you should include the implications for biodiversity and sustainability. (AO1, AO2) 10 marks

a **changes in population**

....

....

....

....

....

....

b economic development

....

....

....

....

....

c agricultural change

....

....

....

....

....

Savanna grasslands

23 **Describe a typical savanna grassland climate. (AO1, AO2)** 3 marks

....

....

....

....

....

24 **The typical soil of the savanna is a ferruginous soil. Draw an annotated soil profile of a ferruginous soil showing the main characteristics. (AO1, AO3)** 4 marks

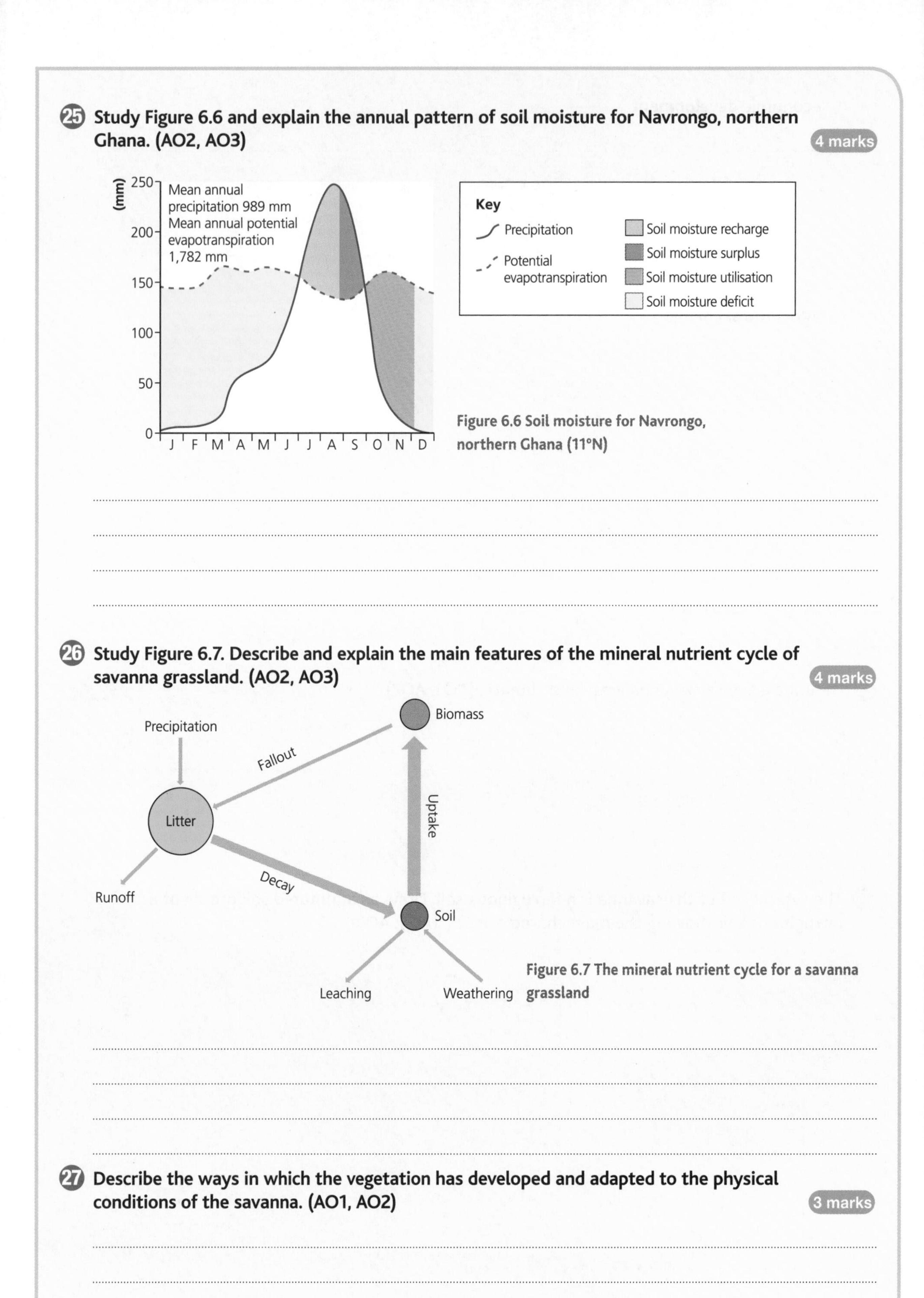

25 **Study Figure 6.6 and explain the annual pattern of soil moisture for Navrongo, northern Ghana. (AO2, AO3)** 4 marks

Figure 6.6 Soil moisture for Navrongo, northern Ghana (11°N)

26 **Study Figure 6.7. Describe and explain the main features of the mineral nutrient cycle of savanna grassland. (AO2, AO3)** 4 marks

Figure 6.7 The mineral nutrient cycle for a savanna grassland

27 **Describe the ways in which the vegetation has developed and adapted to the physical conditions of the savanna. (AO1, AO2)** 3 marks

Ecosystems in the British Isles over time

28 Describe the main characteristics of an ecosystem found in the British Isles that you have studied. (AO1, AO2) 4 marks

....

....

....

....

A plagioclimax community is an area or habitat in which the influence of humans has prevented the ecosystem from developing further. The ecosystem may have been stopped from reaching its full climatic climax or deflected towards a different climax.

29 Using an example of a plagioclimax community in the British Isles (e.g. heather moorland), explain how human intervention has affected the normal seral development. Assess the extent to which the plagioclimax differs from the climatic climax. (AO1, AO2) 20 marks

Write your answer on a separate sheet of paper.

Marine ecosystems

This section concentrates on coral reef ecosystems. Warm-water coral reefs are found around the world where a combination of environmental conditions occurs.

30 Complete Table 6.2 for warm-water coral reefs. (AO1, AO2) 7 marks

Table 6.2

Environmental factor	Ideal conditions for coral development	Reason why the named condition encourages coral growth
Water temperature	26–27°C	
Water salinity		
Clearness of water	Clear water away from silty estuaries	
Water depth		Corals must stay submerged, otherwise they dry out. The shallow depth allows sunlight to penetrate, enabling the *zooxanthellae* algae to photosynthesise
Water turbulence		

31 **Study Figure 6.8.**

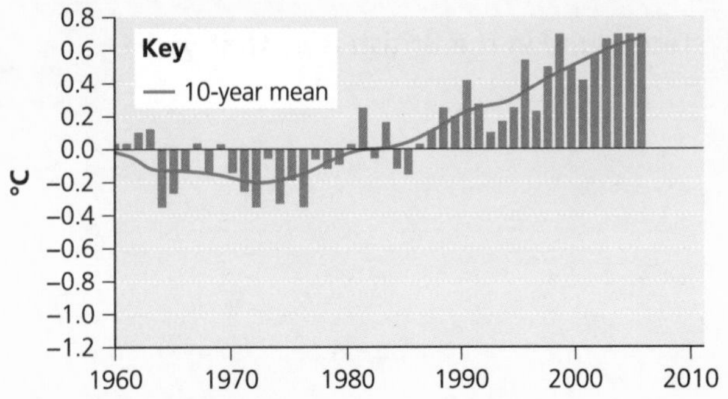

Figure 6.8 Northern hemisphere temperature anomaly, 1960–2005

a **Describe the changes in sea temperatures between 1960 and 2005. (AO3)** 3 marks

....

....

....

b **What problems do these changes in sea temperatures cause for warm-water corals? (AO1, AO2)** 5 marks

....

....

....

....

....

....

32 **Human activity can have a major impact on reefs. Choose two activities from the following list and describe the impact that activity will have on coral reefs. (AO1, AO2)** 8 marks

- **Drainage basin scheme**
- **Onshore development**
- **Introduction of a desalination plant**
- **Tourism**
- **Overfishing**

....

....

....

....

....

....

....

....

....

....

....

....

Local ecosystems

33 For a local ecosystem you have studied:

a **What are the main characteristics of the ecosystem? (AO1, AO2)** 4 marks

....

....

....

b **How have the plants and animals adapted to the local conditions? (AO1, AO2)** 4 marks

....

....

....

c **How has local human activity affected the plants and animals? (AO1, AO2)** 4 marks

....

....

....

d **What conservation measures have been put in place to reduce the impact of changes within the ecosystem? (AO1, AO2)** 4 marks

....

....

Exam-style questions (A-level)

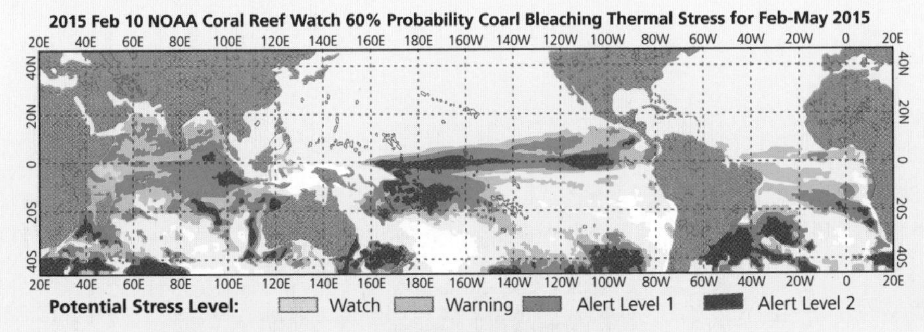

Figure 6.9 NOAA Coral Reef Watch 60% probability coral bleaching — thermal stress for Feb–May 2015

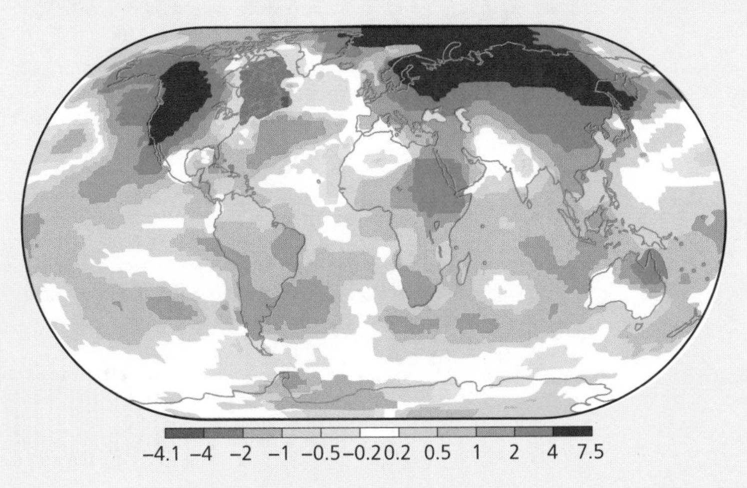

Figure 6.10 Temperature anomalies March 2015 compared to the 1951–1980 mean

Write your answers to questions 1–4 on a separate sheet of paper.

1 **Study Figures 6.9 and 6.10.**

Assess the extent to which the potential stress levels for coral bleaching correlate with the temperature anomalies for March 2015. (AO2, AO3) 7 **6 marks**

2 **Outline the concept of succession and assess the extent to which it could be applied to ONE biome that you have studied. (AO1, AO2)** 11 **9 marks**

3 **Analyse the ecological responses to climate, soil and soil moisture budgets by the flora and fauna of a distinctive local ecosystem that you have studied. (AO1, AO2)** 11 **9 marks**

4 **To what extent do development issues (population change, economic development, agricultural extension and intensification) impact upon the biodiversity and sustainability of TWO contrasting biomes that you have studied? (AO1, AO2)** 25 **20 marks**

Make notes below to plan your answer.

Hodder Education, an Hachette UK company, Blenheim Court, George Street, Banbury, Oxfordshire OX16 5BH

Orders

Bookpoint Ltd, 130 Park Drive, Milton Park, Abingdon, Oxfordshire OX14 4SB
tel: 01235 827827
fax: 01235 400401
e-mail: education@bookpoint.co.uk

Lines are open 9.00 a.m.–5.00 p.m., Monday to Saturday, with a 24-hour message answering service.

You can also order through the Hodder Education website: www.hoddereducation.co.uk

ISBN 978-1-4718-8315-6

First printed 2017

Impression number 8 7 6 5 4 3
Year 2022 2021 2020 2019 2018

Typeset by Aptara, India

Printed in Dubai

Hachette UK's policy is to use papers that are natural, renewable and recyclable products and made from wood grown in sustainable forests. The logging and manufacturing processes are expected to conform to the environmental regulations of the country of origin.